Marquette and Joliet

The
Picture Story
and Biography of

Marquette
and
Joliet

Regina Z. Kelly

ILLUSTRATED BY W. T. MARS

The Library of American Heroes

FOLLETT PUBLISHING COMPANY
CHICAGO

Library of Congress Catalog Card Number: 65-14479

1234567890

Marquette and Joliet

Marquette
and
Joliet

THE PICTURE STORY

Father Jacques Marquette, a young Jesuit priest, came to New France in September, 1666. Father Marquette was very happy to come to America. He was eager to preach Christianity to the Indians.

Father Marquette made friends with a young man named Louis Joliet. Joliet planned to be a trader and explorer. He had heard of a great river that flowed to the south. He hoped to find it.

Father Marquette also hoped to explore far into the wilderness. He wanted to preach to the Indians who lived there.

For a few years, Father Marquette worked among the Indians at different missions. Then one

day he had a visit from Louis Joliet. Louis had good news. He had been chosen to find the great southward flowing river and explore it. Father Marquette was to go with him.

On the morning of May 17, 1673, Father Marquette and Louis Joliet, together with five other men, set out in two canoes. The Indians watched silently as their beloved Black Robe departed.

After about a week, the explorers came to Green Bay. Indians in this vicinity told them the great river was very dangerous, full of monsters and demons, and warned them to turn back. The explorers replied that they had to go on, but that they would be careful.

From Green Bay the party moved into the
Fox River. They stopped for two days at the Jesuit
mission at De Pere. It was fortunate they had this
rest, for the rest of the journey on the Fox River
was very difficult. Between the Fox and the Wisconsin rivers, the men often had to carry their
canoes and equipment.

Friendly Indians told Father Marquette and Joliet that the Wisconsin, which flowed southward, emptied into the great river. On June 17, the men noticed that the Wisconsin River was growing wider and rougher. Soon the river flowed into another broader, fast-moving river, with rounded bluffs, three and four hundred feet high, on both sides. It was the great river — the Mississippi.

As the canoes moved downriver, the hills grew smaller, and now and then there were stretches of prairie. The men saw great herds of huge dark animals running across the prairie. Some of them came to drink at the river's edge. The men stared, for none of them had seen buffalo before.

The explorers traveled 175 miles on the Mississippi River without meeting any Indians. Then Father Marquette and Joliet followed tracks that led away from the river. They came to a village of the Illinois Indians, where they were greeted in friendship. The Indian chief asked Father Marquette to stay in their village, telling him it was dangerous to go on. When he saw they were determined to go, he gave them a young boy called White Owl and a pipe that was a symbol of peace among the Indians.

A few days after leaving the Illinois Indians, the explorers rounded a bend in the river and came upon a frightening sight. On the flat surfaces of a great rock wall on the river's west bank, two horrible animals were painted. After the first shock of seeing them, Father Marquette and Joliet realized that these must be the terrible monsters the Indians had warned them about.

Soon afterward the explorers reached a place where another big river emptied into the Mississippi. This river, flowing from the northwest, was the Missouri.

On July 11, the explorers came to another Indian village. The Indians advanced threateningly toward them, but Father Marquette stood in the canoe, holding up the calumet of peace. When they saw the peace pipe, the Indians allowed the party to land and gave them food and shelter.

At a village near the Arkansas River, the Indians told the Frenchmen it was very dangerous for them to go on. The Indians to the south were hostile, and the Spaniards who controlled the mouth of the Mississippi would make them prisoners. Father Marquette and Joliet knew this was true, and they had accomplished their purpose, so they decided to turn back. The Indians told them of a shorter route to take, by way of the Illinois River.

On the way back, the party stopped at a large village of the Illinois Indians, called Kaskaskia. They stayed for three days, and Father Marquette preached to the Indians. They were very sad when he left, and the priest promised to return the following year.

Father Marquette and Joliet returned safely to the mission at De Pere, where they spent the

winter. Father Marquette wrote an account of the trip, also describing the plants and animals of each region and the Indians they had visited.

In the spring of 1673, Louis Joliet left De Pere. He took with him the Indian boy, White Owl. He was fond of the boy, and planned to send him to school in Montreal. But White Owl never reached Montreal. Joliet's canoes overturned in the boiling La Chine Rapids near Montreal, and everyone in the party except Joliet was drowned. His instruments and all his records of the trip were lost too.

Father Marquette's courage was always greater than his strength, and the long trip had left him weak. But after a rest, he was again traveling among the tribes, preaching to the Indians.

Early in 1675, his sickness grew worse. Father Marquette knew he would not live long. He wanted to return to his mission at De Pere, but he died on the journey on May 1, 1675. His faithful companions buried the beloved Black Robe according to his instructions, on a little rise of ground on the eastern shore of Lake Michigan.

Father Marquette's name and that of Louis Joliet live on in history and in many monuments and markers all over the rich and fertile region they opened for the millions who came after them.

Marquette
and
Joliet

THE BIOGRAPHY

CHAPTER

1

The young priest stood at the prow of the big sailing vessel with the captain, as they slowly drew near the western shore of the St. Lawrence River. Near them were a dozen young girls, holding tight in the stiff breeze to their hooded cloaks, all gazing with shining eyes at the frowning rock precipice they were approaching.

Quebec! *"Quel bec!* . . . What a nose!" Champlain had cried when he had first seen it. The great stone nose still was thrust disdainfully into the swirling waters of the river.

"You can see the Upper and Lower towns now,

Father Marquette," said the captain as the ship drew parallel to the river's bank.

The eyes of the young priest looked swiftly up and down. "There is a difference in the buildings," said he, "and the life, I suppose."

"The government and the church live up there," answered the captain. "The merchants and the workmen live down here. The mountain road ties them together." He pointed to the narrow, winding path that ran steeply down the side of the precipice.

Here and there through autumn's blaze of russet and gold, Father Marquette could see the thick log walls and block houses of the barricade around the Upper Town. Gray stone turrets of big buildings peered above the walls. The slender spires of church steeples pierced the bright blue of the sky. At the very edge of the precipice was a massive stone structure. The white flag of France with its golden fleur de lis flew from one of its high towers.

"That is the citadel," said the captain, following the priest's gaze. "It holds the St. Lawrence like a great stone fist. The governor lives there in the Chateau St. Louis."

The governor of New France! What a mighty empire he rules from the fortress town of Quebec, thought Father Marquette. But it had taken France more than half a century to make that hold secure.

Fishermen from Normandy and Brittany in France had come each year to Newfoundland since John Cabot had discovered it in 1497, but they had made no permanent settlements. In 1534, an expedition under Jacques Cartier had explored the St. Lawrence Gulf and River and had made a short-lived settlement at Montreal. For nearly seventy years after that, there had been no further settlement, though the fishermen still continued to come.

Then in 1604, members of a French trading company, which included Samuel de Champlain, had made a settlement at Port Royal in Acadia or Newfoundland. This also was unsuccessful, but out of it had come the founding of Quebec in 1608 by Champlain. France now had a foothold in the New World, and through the efforts of Champlain, justly called, "The Father of New France," the colony had survived.

In the meantime, England, Holland, and Portugal had firmly established their colonies in North America. It was not until Cardinal Richelieu became the chief minister of Louis XIII that New France made real progress. Richelieu was determined that France should have her share of the riches of North America. In 1627, he organized a colonizing company called The Company of the

Hundred Associates, because of its one hundred wealthy merchant-stockholders. The Company was given a monopoly of the fur trade in America. In return, it had to send at least two hundred settlers each year to New France, and provide for them until they became self-supporting. Under the Company, only Catholics and Frenchmen were allowed to become settlers, and thus from the beginning, through these restrictions, the French colony was doomed to failure.

In 1660, the Company lost its charter because it had failed to bring enough settlers. By this time, Louis XIV was King of France with Jean Baptiste Colbert as his very able finance minister. Colbert was "the work-ox of Louis XIV." Not only did he start trading companies to colonize in North America, but also in India and Africa. He had put a protective tariff on goods coming into France, in order to develop French trade and industries.

Colbert will make New France great and prosperous. One day we'll rival England in trade and colonies, thought Father Marquette as he studied the towering precipice of Quebec.

The ship was almost at the shoreline now. Here the buildings were smaller and clustered together. Smoke curled from the chimneys of fifty or more rough-built homes. There were a few larger houses of wood or stone. A big warehouse with two towers and wide wings was in the midst of the houses. A small church with a belfry was near the beach.

The deck of the ship began to bustle with activity. The anchor was lowered, a gangplank pulled into place, and bales and barrels pushed forward. The crowd on the wharf now could be plainly seen.

"There are the Jesuit fathers to welcome you," said the captain.

He nodded toward three priests who stood at the water's edge. Their long black robes and wide shovel-shaped hats were the same as Father Marquette's. They peered up at the boat and gravely took off their hats to salute him. He waved his own hat in return.

In 1625, through the efforts of Champlain, who was deeply religious, four Jesuits had come to Quebec to serve as missionaries to the Indians. Their progress in converting the Indians had been slow. Many of the first priests had been horribly tortured, and some had suffered death by the hands of those they had tried to convert. But with extraordinary courage and zeal, they had continued their efforts. The days of martyrdom were over now. There were missions in Quebec, Montreal, Three Rivers and Tadoussac on the St. Lawrence and smaller missions along the Great Lakes as far as the western end of Lake Superior.

How wonderful that at last I am here to help carry on their work, thought Father Marquette. Once more, he waved his hat to the priests who waited below on the wharf.

A middle-aged woman in rich black silk, with a servant in a flaring cap and full-skirted apron, stood near the priests.

"That is Madame Bourdon," said the captain. "She brought over the first shipload of wives for our men in Quebec. Now she takes charge of each arrival."

Madame Bourdon nodded and smiled at the girls who, with a stout, matronly woman, stood behind Father Marquette. All curtseyed to Madame Bourdon. The young women were the "King's girls," who had come to marry the colonists in New France. The older woman had been employed by the King to take charge of the girls until they arrived in Quebec. The Ursuline nuns in France had trained the girls in housewifery, and the King had given them a dowry. He would give them other generous gifts when they married, and a bounty for each one of their children.

The wharf was filled now with well-dressed gentlemen giving orders; clerks busy with notebooks and quill pens; farmers unloading their broad-bottomed boats piled high with produce; and fur traders in deerskin jackets and caps.

About fifty or more men had crowded to the side of the boat where the passengers were standing. Some were farmers, or clerks, or minor army officers. Others, more rough-looking, were trying to push their way to the front. They were dressed in clean cotton shirts and pantaloons, and it was evident they had bathed and had trimmed their beards and long, matted hair. Bright colored ribbons and feathers were thrust into their red knitted caps.

"Those are the voyageurs," said the captain to Father Marquette. "They also hope to be bridegrooms. They have not dressed in their Sunday best for you, Father."

The life of a voyageur was hard, explained the captain. It took its toll in strength very soon. Most of the voyageurs wanted to become farmers when they were older.

As the girls drew near the gangplank, one turned her head away and pinched her cheeks until they were rosy. Another shifted her hood until her dark curls fell forward on her shoulders. Father Marquette smiled a little. He guessed there would be three proposals of marriage for each girl in the group. There was no need for more adornment.

"I doubt if any of these voyageurs has much chance to get a bride," said the captain, who was also grinning at his young women passengers. "The first question these girls will ask their suitors is, 'Do you have a house and farm?'"

A few minutes later, Father Marquette strode down the gangplank and knelt to receive the blessing of Father le Mercier, the superior-general of the Jesuits in New France.

"Yours is the seventh ship of the fleet to arrive," said Father le Mercier after he had introduced the other priests. "Only one more is due."

The superior had been told that a fleet of eight ships was to come from France with food and supplies. So far, he told Father Marquette, the ships had landed safely, although several had been pursued by English or Turkish ships.

"Our ship was chased by an English man-of-war, but we managed to escape," said Father Marquette. He knew that countries in Europe were almost constantly at war. News of peace traveled slowly, and sea captains did not hesitate to attack the ship of another country, if they thought it could be captured.

There were courteous questions then from the superior about the voyage of Father Marquette. It had lasted three months, he said. Their boat, which was small, had been storm-tossed, and nearly everyone had suffered from seasickness and ship fever.

The girls now also were on land and were being checked by Madame Bourdon. "I hope you did not give Father Marquette any trouble," he heard her say.

The girls made eager comments. "Oh, no. He was always so gay and friendly. He was like a big brother to us."

For a moment, Father Marquette's face grew wistful. It was so long since he had seen his own family. He had been the youngest of six children from a family of soldiers, statesmen, and men of great wealth. His devout mother had helped to influence his decision to become a priest. But true to his background, he had decided to join the Jesuit order, who were famous not only as scholars, but as diplomats and men who fought for a cause. He had entered the Jesuit college at Nancy in 1654 when he was seventeen, and had rarely seen his family after that. Perhaps, he would never see them again.

The girls were leaving now, with the servant leading and Madame Bourdon and the matron who had come with the girls in the rear. The voyageurs had edged toward the group and were nudging each other and whispering loudly as they looked. The girl with the dark curls turned her head a little when the group moved forward. A voyageur pretended to follow. Another thrust out his bare foot and the first one sprawled on the ground. There was a scuffle between the two men and shrieks of laughter from the others.

"Tck! Tck!" said Madame Bourdon, shaking a warning finger at the men.

There was much cap-lifting and bowing from the voyageurs. "There will be no wedding bells for you, Pierre! And you, too, Jean!" they cried. Jean and Pierre looked horrified, and bowed even deeper than the rest.

Up the steep and winding path to the Upper Town, Father Marquette now followed the three priests. He stopped for breath as they clambered up the last rugged bit. The other priests waited. They had trudged briskly ahead with scarcely a pause, talking as they climbed.

"Was the climb too much for you, Father Marquette?" asked the superior. His eyes looked worried. The provincial who was the head of the Order in France had highly recommended this new missionary because of his devoutness and special ability to learn languages. It was so important to have priests in New France who could speak the Indian dialects. But was Father Marquette not strong enough for the rigors of the life ahead of him?

"I am not at all tired," said the young priest. "I have climbed the hills of Laon, where I was born, since my childhood. It is this wonderful view that takes my breath away." He wanted to believe this. God could not fail him now.

There was a feast that day with a gift of three capons and a dozen pigeons from Governor Courcelles, and a box of precious raisins and prunes from the Ursuline nuns. The Mother Superior also sent Father Marquette four linen sheets and an embroidered altar cloth in thanks for his care during the voyage of the girls who were now under her charge in the convent.

"Have husbands been found for all the young girls?" Father Marquette asked the superior, remembering how eagerly they had looked forward to their new life and new husbands.

Father le Mercier smiled. "Mother Superior told me that all had been promised before she sent us our gifts. There were dozens of young men turned away, though all, except the voyageurs, could show that they possessed land and that they had a good income."

"Will the young couples get more gifts from the King?" asked Father Marquette.

"They will go home with loaded boats," answered the superior. "Each couple will get a cow, a pair of swine, some chickens, two barrels of salted meat and some money."

"And when will the marriages take place?"

"On Sunday, at a nuptial Mass," said the superior. "Sunday is our market day. All the farm families come here on Saturday with their produce. We shall have a fine celebration after the Mass, and then our young people will go down the river to their farms."

Later that day, Father Marquette had a private interview with Father le Mercier. "You will have to live with the Indians, if I send you on a mission," said the superior. "Although the Iroquois no longer torture and kill our priests as they did in the past, you may have to suffer many hardships. Often, you may be without food and shelter."

Father Marquette nodded. He was remembering the stories in the many volumes of the *Jesuit Relations* he had read in the dim, cold libraries of the Jesuit schools. The books contained digests of the annual reports of the missionaries in New France. The authors were educated men, who had been trained to observe and record. They were explorers and scientists as well as men of God. They had written of the natural features of this vast new land; of the strange manner of living and character of the Indians; and the moving stories, frequently

30

told by others, of hardships, torture, and even martyrdom of the priests.

From the time Father Marquette had read the first report, he had longed to come to New France. For years he had waited patiently for permission from his superiors. Jesuit priests were like soldiers in an army in their unquestioning obedience to commands. Time after time, Father Marquette's request to come to America had been denied. The reasons had never been made clear to him, and he had wondered why. Was it because he was needed as a teacher at home? Was his ability to learn languages of greater value to the Order of Jesuits in France? Or was it because he did not look strong? That was what the superior thought now, guessed Father Marquette. Dear God! Let me convince him otherwise, he prayed. Give me strength.

"I have read in the *Jesuit Relations* about the hardships of which you tell me now," said Father Marquette, his eyes shining as he spoke. "I am twenty-nine years old, but since I became a novice I have longed to be like Saint Francis Xavier," he continued eagerly. "Like him, I have studied many languages, and now I also want to spread the gospel in strange lands and, perhaps, even die in the wilderness. God will make my body as strong as my heart and my will."

Father le Mercier looked at the young priest. He was slender and not very tall. His face was clean shaven and his long straight hair fell to his shoulders. His mouth was wide and firm, his chin strong. There was color now in his sallow cheeks. His deep-set, dark eyes glowed as if he saw God's hand held out to him.

Something of the fervor of that devotion warmed Father le Mercier's own heart, and he was ashamed that he had doubted for a moment the young priest's will and ability to be a missionary. "I will write to Father Druillets at Three Rivers to expect you about the middle of October," he said. "Three Rivers is about seventy-seven miles from here and our first mission. Father Druillets will instruct you in the Indian dialects."

That night, the superior made an entry in his journal. "Sept. 20, 1666. Father Jacques Marquette arrived in good health on the 7th ship."

Father le Mercier was certain now that the "heart and will" of the young priest would give him the strength he needed.

CHAPTER

2

For several weeks, Father Marquette remained in Quebec, living in the big stone house of the Jesuits. There were six priests in the house and four seminarians, young men who were studying for the priesthood.

Father Marquette took an instant liking to the youngest student, twenty-one-year-old Louis Joliet. He was stocky and darkskinned, with thick black hair and a merry, impudent grin. Unlike the other students, who were the sons of rich merchants or from noble families, Louis had been born near Quebec and was the son of a poor wagon maker who had died when Louis was only about six years old.

"He was so devout as a boy and so bright," said Father le Mercier to Father Marquette, "that I offered to let him study here when he said he wanted to become a priest."

"Is he making good progress?" asked Father Marquette.

"He is an excellent student. Last year, he was our clerk of the church and took part in a public debate on philosophy. But now he doubts if the priesthood is his true vocation."

Father Marquette was surprised. "What does he want to do instead?"

"Become a fur trader and explorer. His two brothers, Adrien and Zachary, are fur traders, and the Joliets are a close-knit family. Louis has talked the matter over with Monsignor Laval, who is the head of our church in Quebec, and the Monsignor, I believe, will give Louis permission to leave our Order."

"Do you think he has made a wise choice?" asked Father Marquette doubtfully. He knew that Louis had taken only the first vows of a priest which were not binding, but he was surprised that those in charge of the church in Quebec seemed willing to have the young man give up the priesthood.

Father le Mercier nodded. "Louis is young,

vigorous, and enterprising. He will serve God as well as France, if he becomes an explorer. The farther we spread our control in New France, the more Indians will be brought into the faith, and that, as you know, is our main purpose in coming to this land." U. S. 1486413

It was Louis Joliet who became Father Marquette's chief guide around Quebec. There was something alike in the two young men. Both were friendly and easy-mannered and quick to laugh at small things. Both were fervent in their devotions, and deep in their attachment to their church and their country. Both had high courage and a love of adventure.

With Louis as a guide, Father Marquette walked the narrow cobbled streets of the town. The top of the rocky precipice was crowded with the buildings of the church and government and the residences of the officials of both. Governor Courcelles lived in the Chateau St. Louis on the highest side of the great square where the soldiers drilled. On the other sides of the square were the quarters for the soldiers.

A little distance from the square were the convent and gardens of the Ursuline nuns who conducted the school for girls. Near it was the Hotel Dieu, the hospital in charge of the Hospital nuns.

The house of the Jesuits and their church were across from the great cathedral of Notre Dame, which had been built by Champlain. Behind the cathedral was the house of Monsignor Laval and his seminary for young men studying for the priesthood. All of the buildings were of stone and were massive and solid looking.

Monsignor Francis Xavier Laval had come to Quebec in 1659 when he was thirty-six years old. He was a very devout man, and although he was descended from a wealthy and noble French family, he lived in poverty in Quebec and denied himself every comfort. The Jesuits found him a good friend, for he admired them and sympathized with their desire not only to convert the Indians but to add to the knowledge of the country. Laval was equally devoted to the welfare of Quebec and the education of its young people. Not only did he found a seminary, but also a school for both Indian and white boys, and a farm school in the country. In 1674, he was to become the first bishop of Quebec.

"Quebec reminds me of Laon in France, where I was born and where my family have lived for generations," Father Marquette told Louis. "It is also a fortress on a hillside."

"I have heard of Laon," said Louis. "It has repelled attacks of invaders a dozen times."

Father Marquette nodded. He was too modest to relate the part his own family had played in those attacks. They were wealthy and important now and married into the royal family. His father, Nicholas Marquette, had been banished for a time for supporting Henry IV, but had returned to Laon and been richly rewarded when the King had regained his power. Something of the determined spirit of Laon and the Marquettes was part of the fibre of Father Marquette, in spite of the priest's gentle calling.

Each day with Louis, Father Marquette visited the Hotel Dieu, where the sick Indians were treated. The priest marvelled to see the nuns, most of them daughters of rich and important families, so patient in their care of the dirty, insect-ridden savages. The Indians were as grateful as children and swarmed to the hospital. He told Louis of his surprise.

"The Indians will not take care of their own sick," said Louis. "They let those who have little hope for recovery die in the woods."

"Why do the Hospital nuns who are here wear brown robes?" asked Father Marquette. "In France, they are dressed in white."

"The three nuns who came here in 1639 wore white habits," said Louis. "But in a week's time, their clothes were so grease-stained that they boiled their habits in dye made from birch bark, and they have worn brown habits ever since."

As the two young men walked and visited, Joliet told of his own plans for the future. "Father le Mercier will give me letters to the men who were in the Company of the One Hundred Associates," he said. "Even though the Company no longer controls the fur trade in New France, I hope my letters will get me a commission to explore. I should like to go to Lake Superior to search for copper."

"The Jesuits tell about the search for copper in the *Relations*," said Father Marquette, his interest roused at the thought of discovering new things and places. He told Louis what he had read, and Louis nodded agreement as the priest spoke. The Indians mined for copper in a rude way and made it into utensils and ornaments. But they believed that powerful spirits lived in the veins of the ore, and would punish them if they told the whites where the copper could be found.

"That is why, so far, we have not found the mines," said Louis. "Those who have explored believe the copper can be found on the southeastern shore of Lake Superior and on Isle Royale in the lake. But the Indians are afraid to go there. That is why I wish to go to Lake Superior myself."

Father Marquette looked wistful. "I would

like to go with you and carry the gospel to the savages who must live in these strange places."

Joliet smiled at him confidently. "Perhaps, when I return from France, we will both be sent in search of souls and copper. I should like to search for the 'great river' also."

"And so should I," said Father Marquette eagerly. "I have read about the 'great river' in the *Relations*. The Indians have told our priests that it flows into the Gulf of Mexico. They seem to know little more than that."

"Perhaps, instead, it flows into the Gulf of California," said Joliet. "If that is so, we would discover a new way to China."

The faces of both men grew bright at the thought. From the earliest days of exploration, men of all nationalities had hoped to find a waterway in North America that would take them to the Pacific Ocean and thence to China. So certain had Cartier been that the St. Lawrence River was this waterway, that he had called the rapids south of Montreal, "La Chine," because he thought they blocked his way to China.

In 1634, Champlain had sent Jean Nicolet, a trader and explorer, to find the "Sea of China." Nicolet had gone as far as the Wisconsin River. He had been so certain that he would meet with the

Chinese, that he had brought a ceremonial robe of Chinese damask with him. Now once again, Frenchmen were hoping to find this waterway to China.

"It is strange that the Indians have not followed the 'great river' to its mouth," said Father Marquette. "Many of the Indians I have read about must live near the river or cross it in their travels."

"Indians have so little curiosity," said Joliet impatiently. "They move to new places only when they are pursued by an enemy or in need of food. Only the white man will explore."

In his first days at Quebec, Father Marquette made courtesy calls on Monsignor Laval, on Governor Courcelles, and on the Intendant, Jean Talon. Governor Courcelles was the military leader of New France, but the Intendant was almost as powerful, for he controlled the courts of justice and the treasury.

Father Marquette found his visit with the Intendant to be rewarding and interesting. He soon discovered that Jean Talon was an intelligent and energetic man who was interested in having the west explored to add to the glory and wealth of New France. He was a fine-looking man with well-formed features and a full wig of dark curls falling to the wide lace collar of his red velvet coat. But in spite of his elegant appearance, Father Marquette could see that the Intendant was vigorous and energetic and capable himself of going on one of the expeditions he was so eager to send to the west.

"I am especially anxious to find out if there is a waterway to the China Sea," said Talon, "and to search for the copper mines to the west."

The priest related what he and Joliet had discussed about the possibility of copper deposits on Isle Royale and the shores of Lake Superior.

"I have also heard these stories," said the Intendant, "and I know young Joliet. I may send him on an expedition when he returns from France. The Indians also tell about a river which is as wide and beautiful and deep as the St. Lawrence, and which may empty into the China Sea. Perhaps, Joliet could also search for the river."

"If that waterway is found, the Jesuits, no doubt, will start missions along the route," said Father Marquette. He knew that the Intendant thought highly of the Order of the Jesuits and their work in New France.

Talon smiled a little. He had caught the yearning note in the voice of the young priest. "The explorer, then the missionary, then the fur trader. That is the history of the growth of power in New France," he said.

After his visit with the Intendant, Father Marquette walked along the embankment that over-looked the St. Lawrence. He stared long at the river. "A waterway as wide and beautiful and deep as the St. Lawrence," he said to himself. "If Joliet is sent there, perhaps . . . But I am too new and untried. Dear Saint Francis Xavier, let me but follow in your path."

CHAPTER

3

FATHER GABRIEL Druillets was in charge of the Jesuit mission at Three Rivers, which was about seventy-seven miles south of Quebec. Although Three Rivers was an early settlement and fur trading post, it was still not very large. The mission, however, was in excellent hands. Father Druillets was not only well acquainted with Indian ways and character, but he was an expert in languages. He even knew a little English, for in 1650, he had been sent to Massachusetts to suggest an alliance between the French and English against the Iroquois. The New Englanders had been friendly to the priest, even though they had rejected his offer of alliance.

"The Indian dialects are quite difficult," he warned Father Marquette during their first lesson. "You will have to memorize every word. We have no grammar or dictionary, and sometimes the same word has several meanings. Some of our priests find the dialects impossible to learn, and we have to send them to a white settlement."

However, Father Marquette was an apt pupil. In the two years he remained at Three Rivers, he learned five Indian dialects. But there was more to his training than the study of languages.

"A missionary has to live as the Indians do, if he is to win their friendship," Father Druillets constantly reminded his pupil. "You must learn their tastes and character, their beliefs and practices, and the qualities they like and admire in others."

The Indians in North America were grouped into five great families, Father Druillets explained. They were the Hurons in Canada; the Algonquins south of the Great Lakes; the Iroquois around Lake Erie in the heart of the Algonquin territory; the Southern Indians below the Algonquins; and the Sioux to the far west.

The Jesuits, so far, had worked chiefly with the Hurons and the Algonquins. When Champlain had been governor of New France, he had aided the Hurons in a battle against the Iroquois on Lake Champlain. The gunfire of the French had so terrified the Iroquois that they had fled without fighting, but ever after they had hated the French. This was unfortunate, for although the Iroquois were small in numbers, they were the best organized and the fiercest warriors among the great families. It was the Iroquois who had been most cruel to the Jesuits who had come into their land.

"We are never able to travel on the Great Lakes because the Iroquois control Lake Erie," said Father Druillets. "They have promised now not to make war against the French, but they still will not let Frenchmen or Indians who trade with Frenchmen come into their territory."

In April, 1668, Father Marquette was given his first assignment as a missionary. He was to go to the mission at Sault Sainte Marie, in the country of the Ottawas, who belonged to the Algonquin family. A sturdy Canadian boy and two donnés, Jules and Martin, would go with him to Montreal, where they would leave with a trading party for the Sault. The donnés were French laymen who served the missionaries without pay. Like many other devout Frenchmen, the donnés gave their services to the missionaries for the love of God.

From Montreal, the party was to travel by way

of the Ottawa River and its branches into Georgian Bay and then into Lake Huron to the Sault. This was a difficult route, using rivers and portages, but necessary because of the Iroquois control of Lake Erie.

Jules, one of the donnés, and two Indians were in the canoe with Father Marquette when the party left Montreal. As he made ready to wade out to the boat, the priest said a little prayer to Saint Francis Xavier to help him remember what Father Druillets had taught him. It was so important from the beginning to win the respect of the Indians.

Carefully, Father Marquette took off his shoes and stockings and tucked his cassock high in his belt, so as not to drag sand and pebbles into the canoe. When he was seated, he removed his wide hat and replaced it with the cap he wore at night. Then he picked up a paddle and knelt on the rush mat. Two men at a time would paddle.

"You need not take the paddle, Father," said Jules. "We will divide the paddling among the three of us."

He thinks I will not have the strength to continue paddling all day, thought Father Marquette. To stop paddling, once one began, was considered a sign of weakness by the Indians. "I will take my turn," said the priest quietly.

The hours wore on. There would be no stop until evening, for only two meals a day were eaten. By afternoon, every bone and muscle in Father Marquette's body ached and burned. With half-shut eyes, he prayed with dry lips when he was relieved, but, somehow, he picked up the paddle when it was his turn again.

At sunset, the canoe was anchored and the men waded to the land. Only when a storm threatened were the canoes beached, for the rough shore might cut the delicate bark covering of the canoes. Although there had been rain the previous night, this day the wind and weather had helped them make good time. "We traveled twenty miles," the leader of the group announced.

The donnés lit the fire and cooked the evening meal. With nodding head, Father Marquette leaned against a tree and read from his breviary. This was a book of daily prayers and readings for a priest. Once he noticed that the Indians were having trouble starting a fire with the damp wood, and he offered them the use of his flint and steel. The two donnés smiled approval. Later, the Indians brought Father Marquette and his companions some fish which they had broiled on hot stones.

When the white men were ready to wrap themselves in their blankets for the night, one of the

Indians brought Father Marquette a small earthen jar of fat.

"It is bear grease, Father," said Jules. "Rub it on your shoulders and legs before you go to sleep. It will ease the pain in your muscles."

After a few days, the soreness from paddling ended for the young priest. Now after supper, Father Marquette walked up and down while he read his prayers. Sometimes, he sang the words aloud, and the Indians would draw close to listen. He knew they might think his little black book had magic if he said the prayers to himself. Furthermore, they liked singing, and chanted their own tuneless songs on every occasion. When Father Marquette saw his audience grow restless, he hurried his prayers a little. Jules and Martin nodded at each other. The new priest understood the savages.

At last, the party came to the "Sault" which was the French word for waterfall. Here there was a large village of Ojibwas, an Algonquin tribe, but many other Indians also came to the Sault, for food was abundant. A mission had been started there thirty years before, but it was hard to make the wandering Indians remain Christians. The Sault was also an important trading post.

"We must do what we can to keep the savages

in one place," Father Marquette told his donnés, after they were settled at the mission. "If we build a permanent home and plant crops, they may do the same."

Soon the white men cleared a piece of land and built a bark-covered hut in which to live. The front part was the chapel and the back part their home. When the chapel was ready, Father Marquette arranged his altar and hung up a crucifix and some bright colored pictures.

The Sault abounded in whitefish. The huge cascade of water from Lake Superior tumbled down the rocks. At its foot, the young Indians stood upright in their tossing canoes. Father Marquette marvelled, as he watched them thrust long poles with a net on the end into the whirling waters. With a sudden strong jerk, the Indians would pull the poles upward, and toss six or seven large fish into their boat.

There was other food besides the fish. The squaws planted corn, squash, beans, and pumpkins. In the woods apples, cherries, grapes and all kinds of berries grew wild. But the savages ate the fruits greedily before they were half ripe. The children brought the priest baskets of blueberries which were as large as grapes.

Father Marquette had never seen these berries

before, and he found them delicious when mixed with the tasteless sagamité which was the daily fare of the Indians. Sagamité was made of cornmeal which the Indians had ground between two stones. Then it was put into a container made of birch bark that was filled with water. Hot stones were added to the water until it boiled and the cornmeal became mush. Sometimes fish, meat, or bits of fat were added to the mush, or berries such as Father Marquette ate and enjoyed.

The white men thriftily dried and stored the berries for the winter months. The Indians, however, ate gluttonously whenever they were hungry, and stored only the food they could not possibly devour.

"They eat as if they never expect to see food again," Father Marquette remarked to his donnés when first he had seen the greed of the Indians.

"Perhaps they will have little to eat this winter," said Martin. "But you will find out that they will never complain. Somehow, white men never seem to be able to follow the same pattern, and so they suffer more when they are hungry."

There were other new facts which Father Marquette learned about the Indians, now that he lived with them. He noticed that the women were modest and always completely covered in their dress, though the men were almost naked except in the winter. In spite of their hard and patient work, the squaws were frequently mistreated by the braves.

Father Marquette was unable to make the braves think this was cruel, nor was he able to make them agree that lying, cheating, or stealing was wrong.

"It is the custom of our tribe," they would answer his protest, and wonder why the Black Robe said they ought not to do these things, and should ask the Great Spirit for forgiveness.

It was not long before Father Marquette came into conflict with the medicine men of the tribes. Most of them were old, evil-looking men who carried bags of animal bones and ornaments which they used when attempting to cure the sick. But they also used herbs and ointments, and in this way often cured an Indian and thus maintained their power and received fine presents.

"They are men of magic and will work against you," warned Martin, "because they will lose their influence if you win the Indians to our faith."

Because the Indians were naturally superstitious, it was not hard for the medicine men to make the savages believe there was evil in all of Father Marquette's actions. The sign of the cross was a gesture that would bring peril, the medicine men told the Indians, and water sprinkled on a child in baptism would bring instant death. Unfortunately for Father Marquette, he was frequently asked to baptize a dying child, and so the words of the medicine men seemed to be true.

In spite of the opposition of the medicine men, Father Marquette worked tirelessly. He visited as many Indians as he could, particularly those who were very old or ill. He talked cheerfully to the squaws and caressed the children. He liked small children, but he also knew that the Indians enjoyed this kind of attention. Whenever possible, he induced those who were old to become Christians and be baptized.

"The old people are a sure harvest," he told the donnés. "At least, they will not wander from the faith."

The children in the village loved the gentle young priest and came each day to his little chapel to say their prayers and recite the catechism. Older people also came, but out of curiosity. They watched with childlike delight as the white men used a handmill to grind their corn into meal. They stared wide-eyed when Father Marquette placed his magnifying glass over a flea and made it grow as large as a beetle. They wondered how he could know directions by looking at a little round instrument. They were sure the needle of his compass had a magic voice. His clock, which struck the time, had endless charm for them. They would sit watching it for hours as the hands moved slowly and the steady tick-tock went on.

"What does it say now?" they would ask when the clock struck.

"Time for dinner," he would say at noon. Or, "Time to go home," at four.

"If the Indians will come to see these little tools of civilized men," Father Marquette told the donnés, "perhaps, they will return to hear me tell of God." So patiently, again and again, he showed the savages his small bag of tricks.

After nearly a year and a half at Sault Sainte Marie, Father Marquette was sent to a mission on Lake Superior called La Pointe du Saint Esprit. It meant The Point of the Holy Spirit and was usually called La Pointe. It was a narrow strip of land about six miles long jutting into the southwestern end of Lake Superior and was the farthest western mission of the Jesuits. The French had started a trading post there in 1659, and, six years later, Father Allouez had founded the mission. A younger man was needed now at La Pointe, and so Father Marquette was sent while Father Allouez went to the mission at Green Bay.

The Ottawas, who had fled there from the Iroquois, lived at La Pointe; but many other tribes, including Hurons, also came. It could be reached easily by portages and rivers, and the fishing was good. So far, it had been safe from the Iroquois, who had not traveled this far west.

Father Marquette arrived at La Pointe on September 13, 1669; he soon established himself as at the Sault. Although the Ottawas were friendly, they had little interest in becoming Christians, and he worked mainly with the old people and the children. One day, an old man whom he had been instructing was ill with a high fever.

"Our medicine man says he can drive away the evil spirit that makes my blood boil, if I will give him a new robe," the old man said to Father Marquette. "But I do not want him to pray to his manitou for me, now that I believe in the God of the white man. Help me, Black Robe, for our medicine man is powerful and may do me harm."

From the medicine chest he carried with him, Father Marquette took some dried leaves. Soon he brewed a strong tea and gave it to the old man, and told him to repeat the dose several times during the day.

"You are ready now for baptism," said Father Marquette. "If you become a Christian today, you will have courage and the medicine man will not harm you."

Then, while the donné held the flask of holy water, the priest baptized the old man.

Before leaving him, Father Marquette gave the old man a crucifix. "Hold this before the medicine man, if he comes near you," said the priest, "and you will frighten him away."

The next day, when Father Marquette visited the old man, he was sitting in front of his hut. "The God of the white man has given me back my health," he said, "and the medicine man will never come near me again."

Then the old man beckoned to a fine-looking young Indian. "This is a slave from the Illinois tribe who has been given to me," said he. "I will give him to you. He will teach you the language and the ways of his tribe."

Although Father Marquette had no intention of keeping the young man in captivity, he was delighted with the gift. He had been told by Father Claude Dablon, the new superior at Quebec, that his next mission would be among the Illinois Indians, and he was anxious to learn their dialect.

All that winter, Father Marquette studied with the young Indian. The priest found out that there were two great villages of the Illinois with about eight to nine thousand people, for their land was fertile. Although the Illinois were sun worshippers, they were neither fierce nor cruel, and the Jesuits had been told they were eager to learn about the white man's God.

The young captive was happy when Father Marquette said that he expected to start a mission among the Illinois.

"My people believe that if a Black Robe will come to them, there will be peace everywhere," said the Indian. "Then they will always live in one place, and only the young men will leave to go hunting."

"How far is it to the land of your tribe?" asked Father Marquette.

"About thirty days' journey, and it is a very difficult way. When I was brought here, I crossed a great river which flowed from north to south."

"Does the river empty into the China Sea?" Father Marquette asked eagerly. He was remembering the talks he had had in Quebec with Louis Joliet and the Intendant, Jean Talon. How anxious they had all been to discover this mighty stream to see if it would lead them to China!

"I do not know," said the young Indian. "It must flow southward for a great distance. There are tribes called Shawnees to the south who come to our villages. They have glass beads such as the men from across the sea give to them."

Quickly, Father Marquette wrote to Father Dablon and sent the letter by an Indian who was taking furs to Quebec. "If the Indians will make me a canoe," wrote the priest, "I can explore this river with a Frenchman and this young man who has been given to me. This discovery will give us full knowledge of the South Sea or the Western Sea."

While at La Pointe, Father Marquette learned of an Indian tribe called the Sioux, of whom his own natives were in constant terror. They lived west of the great river and were between the territory of the Hurons and the Illinois. At the time, the Sioux were on good terms with the Illinois, and had promised to let Father Marquette pass through their land on his way to his new mission.

"Perhaps if I send the Sioux some religious pictures, I will teach them through their eyes," Father Marquette said to the elders of the Ottawas and the Hurons. "Then they might want to know something of the white man's God, and all the tribes will live in peace."

The pictures were sent in the spring of 1671. In a few weeks, the messengers came back. The Sioux not only returned the pictures, though with polite greetings to the Black Robe, but they stated that in the fall they would be on the warpath and would drive the Hurons from the land.

"Could you not stay and fight them?" Father Marquette asked the elders who were assembled in council. The spirit of his ancestors, who had always sprung full-armed to man the gray stone walls of Laon, now made him want to resist.

"We are no match for the Sioux," said the chief. "They are so skilled in war that the air is filled with their arrows before we have time to draw our bows. We must flee this place before the next moon."

After long debate, the Ottawas decided to go to an island in the northern part of Lake Huron. The Hurons, however, planned to move to Mackinac Island in the strait between Lake Huron and the Lake of the Illinois, now called Lake Michigan. The Hurons had lived there for a time until they had been driven farther westward by the Iroquois. They knew that fish were plentiful at Mackinac, and that the soil was excellent for farming. Father Marquette said he would go with the Hurons, for the mission of St. Ignace had already been started on the island the year before.

There were busy days of preparation now. Big canoes were built on the shore. The long cedar frames were covered with great squares of birch bark. These were sewn together with the threads made from spruce rootlets. Then the seams were filled with hot pine gum. Those not working on the canoes whittled away at the short, wide paddles of cedar wood for the canoes.

The squaws were equally busy. Stores of dried food were gathered. Skins and rush mats were bound into bales. Clothing, tools, and weapons were loaded into the canoes as soon as they were ready. Very early, on the morning of departure, the young men went through the fields and huts with flaring pine torches and set everything on fire. There would be nothing left for the Sioux when they arrived.

At dawn, Father Marquette said a last mass in his little chapel, then packed his silver chalice and other altar equipment. Slowly, the long line of canoes moved along the base of the tall brownstone cliffs of Lake Superior. In the last canoe were Father Marquette and his donnés. He stood for a moment and made a giant sign of the cross over the departing fleet. Then he knelt on the rush mat and with steady stroke began to paddle his canoe.

CHAPTER

4

I‍T was midsummer of 1671 before the long line of canoes from La Pointe pulled into the four-mile-wide strait between Lake Huron and the Lake of the Illinois. A little east of the middle was a large island, its center rising to a high wooded bluff. Jagged streaks of white showed through the dark foliage.

"The island looks like the humped back of a great turtle," said Father Marquette.

"Michili — mackinac, the great turtle," Martin answered. "That is what the Indians call it."

On a wide stretch of sandy beach, a crowd of

Indians was waiting. Some strode out into the water to help the new arrivals. An advance party had told the reason for the flight of the Hurons from La Pointe, and so there were only welcoming cries and gestures from those on the beach.

With a backward sweep of the paddles, the donnés brought their canoe to a halt. Martin dropped the anchor, and then he and Jules jumped out to hold the canoe while Father Marquette climbed over the side. The water was cold, but so clear that small stones and darting fish could be seen on the smooth brown bottom. The other canoes also were anchored now, and the Indians were splashing to the beach, carrying heavy loads.

There were already many people living at Mackinac, but there was room for more. Fish were abundant; the soil was rich; from the high bluffs an enemy could be easily seen for twenty miles; and the strait was the main passageway between Lake Huron and the Lake of the Illinois.

"It is the key of the door for all the Indians who live in the south," Father Dablon had written to Father Marquette.

As at his two previous missions, Father Marquette and the donnés soon built a combined chapel and home and worked hard to convert the Indians to Christianity. After a year, because the island was crowded, Father Marquette decided to move the little mission of St. Ignace to a sandy stretch of beach on the mainland, about four miles away. It is the present site of St. Ignace, Michigan.

Father Marquette felt he could hold the Indians to their faith. During the autumn, he had baptized two adults and twenty-eight children. When he had gone to the Sault to visit Father Dablon, who was in charge of the mission there, the Indian children had taken care of his little chapel. As soon as they had sighted his returning canoe, the Indians had left their fields and all were on the beach to welcome him.

"I trust that what they do now through respect, one day will be done through desire to be saved," the priest had told the donnés.

"They do it now through love, Father," Martin had said.

"Well, that is one step nearer to God," the priest had answered.

Winter came early in the second year of the mission. "The ice will soon block the strait, and we shall be bound in for the winter," said Father Marquette to Martin as they stood on the beach on the morning of December the eighth.

The priest waved to the Indians who were skillfully paddling their canoes between the ice blocks.

He felt happy this morning. Today was the Feast of the Immaculate Conception and he had had a large attendance at mass. He had noticed many of the young men openly making the sign of the cross. In time, they might come to him for instruction in the faith.

Then he noticed that some of the canoes had halted, and that several of the Indians were standing and peering toward the east. Father Marquette shaded his eyes from the glare of the snow and also looked. A large canoe was approaching with three men in fur caps and deerskin coats. Soon the canoe was moving among the ice blocks. One man in front waved his cap and shouted something in the Algonquin dialect.

"They must be Frenchmen from Montreal," said Martin. "They have come just in time to escape the ice."

A delighted smile was on Father Marquette's face. "I think it is — yes, it is Louis Joliet. I recognize him even with his beard." He ran to the edge of the beach with his arms outstretched. "Louis! Louis! Welcome to St. Ignace!" he cried.

In a few minutes, the two men were embracing. Joliet looked older and had a small chin beard and a moustache, but his dark eyes still sparkled, and his muscular figure moved with its old easy grace.

Many of the Indians had returned to the shore and there were excited questions and comments. Martin was helping the voyageurs who had come with Joliet to beach and unload the canoe.

"I came from Montreal by way of the Ottawa River," said Joliet. "Each morning when I saw the ice forming on the banks, I wondered if I'd get here in time."

"But why are you here?" asked Father Marquette. "The last of the traders left weeks ago." He had heard that the Joliet family had started a fur trading company and that Louis did much of the traveling for the family.

"I have wonderful news for you, Father Marquette," said Joliet. He patted a small deerskin case he carried. "Wait until you see the papers I carry."

But it was not until the men were in front of the big fireplace and eating bowls of hot corn soup that Joliet told of his mission. "Do you remember, when we were together in Quebec, how often we talked of the great river that flowed to the south?" he asked, his eyes sparkling. "Well, I have been appointed to head an expedition to explore that river."

Father Marquette's dark eyes were wide with amazement. "But how? Why? The French have talked about such an expedition for years, but have done nothing."

"It takes money to send an expedition," said Joliet with a shrug. "And, so far, our knowledge has been based on the stories of the Indians."

"What had made our government change its policy?"

"My brother Zachary agreed to put up some of the money, and our Intendant, Jean Talon, has at last persuaded King Louis to agree. Both King Louis and Colbert now think that there is nothing more important in New France than the discovery of a passageway to the Gulf of California."

"Was it Talon who selected you?" Father Marquette asked Joliet, remembering the talk he had with the Intendant so many years ago in Quebec. Talon could not have made a better choice for a leader than Joliet, the priest was thinking. He had heard of Joliet through the years. He knew that the young man was brave and trustworthy. By now, he knew several Indian dialects and had displayed tact and prudence when dealing with the savages.

"Talon is ill now and has gone back to France," Joliet answered. "But before he left, he recommended to our new governor, Count Frontenac, that I be sent on the expedition."

"And Frontenac agreed, I suppose."

"Yes. He showed me the letter he had written to Colbert, our first minister. You know how anxious Colbert is to promote French trade. Frontenac wrote him that I was a man of experience and had been near the river, and that I promised to see the mouth." Joliet shrugged his shoulders and grinned a little. "I hope he is right."

"And why is Colbert so anxious to have the river explored?"

"Because of the English. Colbert thinks that if we explore the river, we can claim all the land for France," answered Joliet. "Then we can hem in the English on the Atlantic coast and get control of the fur trade with the Indians. He hopes even to find mines along the banks — copper, lead, iron, maybe, even gold and silver."

The French now had more definite information about the location of copper ore in New France, said Joliet. Large deposits could be seen along the shores of Lake Superior and on Isle Royale in the lake.

"But the Indians are afraid to go to the island," he continued.

Joliet told of how four Indian hunters had landed on Isle Royale and heated stones in order to cook their food in a bark vessel, as was their custom. When the stones were red hot, the Indians

66

found out that they were copper. Later, when the Indians were leaving the island with some of the stones, they heard a deep voice like thunder calling out to them, "Who are these thieves who steal the toys of my children?"

The four hunters had paddled away in terror. Three of them had died on the way home, and the fourth had lived only long enough to tell the people of his village what had happened.

"They have always been afraid of the island," said Joliet. "They call it the 'floating island,' because it appears and disappears with the movement of the wind."

"Our Jesuits believe that the disappearance is caused by the mists that are around the island," said Father Marquette. "But it is hard to overcome the superstitious fears of the savages with facts."

"That is the reason why it has been hard for us to search for copper along the Great Lakes, and why we hope to find it on the banks of the great river," said Joliet.

"If France could find this wealth, and at the same time keep England from spreading her colonies, France would be the greatest power in the world." Father Marquette's voice was a little awed. But his heart was filled with pride in the country of his birth and ancestry.

"But King Louis also wishes to spread Christianity among the savages," continued Joliet, "and so do all of us."

Father Marquette nodded. He knew that Joliet was a deeply religious man. Though love of adventure and desire to win profit from trade were probably his chief interests in making this trip, he was also anxious to convert the savages.

"And so a priest will go along with you," said Father Marquette.

Joliet's face was beaming now. "I conferred with Father Dablon when I was in Quebec, and he recommended you for the mission, and Governor Frontenac agreed. Father Dablon gave me written instructions for you."

Father Marquette looked delighted but puzzled. "But why did they select me? Surely, Father Dablon or Father Allouez has had more experience."

Joliet studied the young priest before he answered. In spite of six years of hardship and discouragement, Father Marquette was still gay and hopeful. Father Dablon had spoken highly of him to Joliet. Courage and endurance Marquette had inherited from his ancestors, but the burning zeal of the martyrs was in his heart. Other priests and traders had learned the Indian dialects and characteristics, but Father Marquette knew how to penetrate their minds and spirits and win them to his cause.

"He is patient, kind, and full of tender love and care for the Indians," Father Dablon had told Joliet. "If any man can win the help of the savages you meet as you journey, it is Father Jacques Marquette."

But Joliet said none of these things to his host. They would embarrass the young priest. "Father Dablon is the superior and is needed in Quebec," said Joliet, "and Father Allouez is too old. Besides, you know the Indian dialects as well as they do, and also have knowledge of the river. Father Dablon told me you are anxious to start a mission among the Illinois, and we will be journeying in their territory. You are the only person he recommended to me when I called upon him to discuss the expedition."

Joliet then told what he had been doing since he and Father Marquette had parted in Quebec. He had spent a year in France, as he had planned. Monsignor Laval had loaned him the money.

"He has been my friend since my student days in Quebec," said Joliet, "and believes that I am able to do what I plan. He also helped to finance me in the fur trade, though my family put up our lands as security for the loan."

After he had returned to New France, Joliet continued, he had gone with several exploring parties in search of copper along Lake Superior. In this way, he had learned the Indian dialects and ways, and heard many stories of the great river flowing to the south.

"About three years ago when I was at the western end of Lake Ontario, I accidentally met La Salle and his party. He is also looking for the great river. He believes he can find it by way of the Ohio."

Father Marquette had heard of Robert Cavalier de La Salle. The young man had come to New France in 1666, the same year as the priest. But La Salle had gone to Montreal, where, through the help of his brother, a Sulpician priest, he had obtained a grant of land at La Chine near Montreal. The Sulpicians were missionaries sent from the Seminary of St. Sulpice in France to convert the Indians. They were favored over the Jesuits by both Governor Frontenac and La Salle.

Through his fur trade with the Indians, La Salle also had learned of the great river, which the Indians called the "Missipi" or "Missip," and he had determined to explore it. To raise funds for an expedition, he had sold the land he had been granted in La Chine. He had traveled as far as the

Ohio River, but had been forced to give up his expedition for lack of funds.

"Do you plan to use La Salle's route?" asked Father Marquette.

"No. I believe that since the Iroquois now permit us to travel on Lake Erie, the best route from Quebec is by way of the Great Lakes and into the Wisconsin River. I made a map for La Salle and showed him this route. I did not know then that I would be selected for this expedition."

"What did he think of your suggestion?"

"He still wished to explore by way of the Ohio."

"What do you intend to do now?"

"I shall stay here for most of the winter, and we can plan for our journey. We should leave as soon as the ice breaks."

A soft glow was in Father Marquette's eyes. "It was the Blessed Virgin who helped you," he said. "You came here on her feast of the Immaculate Conception. I should like to dedicate our journey to her, and if we find the river call it 'Conception' in her honor."

Joliet nodded and both men knelt for a little time in prayer. "And now to bed," said Father Marquette. "We have much to do."

The winter months were filled with work for

the two men. The news had spread that they were going to search for the Mississippi, and information came to them from many sources. Fur traders and Indians stopped at St. Ignace to add their bits of knowledge. Letters came to them from government officials and Jesuit priests.

Although there was no official record of a journey to the Mississippi, Frenchmen had gone to places that were thought to be only a few days' travel from the great river. In 1634, Champlain had sent Jean Nicolet to find the "Sea of China." He had explored Lake Huron as far as Mackinac, and then had gone by way of Green Bay and the Fox River to the village of the Mascoutens on the Wisconsin River. Perhaps, because he was disappointed to find only savages, he had not traveled farther, although the Indians had told him that he was only three days' journey from the "great river."

Fathers Dablon and Allouez had also journeyed as far as the village of the Mascoutens, which was near the Wisconsin River. "It is a beautiful river, running southwest without any rapids," Father Dablon had said of the Wisconsin. "The Indians say it leads to the great river called Mississippi, which is about six days' journey from their village." But the two priests also had not continued their journey.

Both Father Marquette and Joliet made careful notes of all that they learned. "We must take every precaution in our power," said the priest. "Our undertaking may be hazardous, but it should not be foolhardy."

They planned to go by way of Green Bay to the Fox River and then portage to the Wisconsin River. It was the same route followed by Nicolet and Fathers Dablon and Allouez. Other Jesuits had also gone part of this way, and the mission of Saint Francis Xavier had been established at De Pere on the Fox River.

Early in the spring, Joliet went to the Sault, for the warehouse of his family's trading company was there. Here he exchanged furs which he had collected through the winter for articles to trade or to be given to the Indians they would meet. He also engaged three voyageurs to be in the canoe with Father Marquette. They were Pierre Porteret, Jacques Largillier, and Pierre Moreau, who was called La Toupine to distinguish him from Pierre Porteret. The two voyageurs who had traveled with Joliet from Montreal would be in his canoe.

The ice began to break in the beginning of May. At the same time, Father Philip Piercon, a young and vigorous priest about thirty years old, came to take Father Marquette's place at St. Ignace.

"We should be able to start about the middle of May," said Joliet as he watched a huge block of ice drift away. "Tomorrow we will begin to pack."

"With the help of God," said Father Marquette, "the great river should soon be made known to the world."

CHAPTER

5

GREAT PUFFS of clouds floated over the deep blue of the sky and a gentle breeze blew on the morning of May 17, 1673. Father Marquette had said Mass at dawn and a crowd of Indians had paddled across the four-mile stretch of water from Mackinac Island to attend the service, and to say good-bye to their Black Robe.

Now, with the Indians at St. Ignace, they crowded the waterfront and silently watched the seven white men prepare to leave on their expedition. Their beloved Black Robe was going away on a perilous journey. Would he ever return? Strange monsters and evil spirits were in those far-distant waterways to which the white men were going. Hostile tribes might attack them. This new Black Robe, Father Piercon, was kind and good, but he was a stranger to their ways.

Joliet, in blanket coat and beaver hat, gave crisp directions to the voyageurs, while Father Marquette discussed last-minute instructions with Father Piercon. The voyageurs swung the big packs of merchandise for gifts and exchange to their backs; fastened them to their deerskin headbands; then moved easily to the canoes. A voyageur could carry a hundred pounds this way. Each man next put his own small bundle of clothing and wad of tobacco into place.

Dried corn and smoked meat were the only food being taken along, for the men expected to fish and kill game on the way, and the woods were full of berries. In a sturdy box were a compass and instruments for measuring latitude and the depth of water; razors and whetstone; needles and thread; and a supply of quill pens, rough paper, and ink. Father Marquette's altar stone and his vessels for saying Mass were carefully wrapped in birch bark. Like the voyageurs, his and Joliet's bundles of extra clothes were small.

The men made ready to wade out to the canoes.

Father Marquette embraced Father Piercon and Joliet shook his hand. "God's blessing be on you," said Father Piercon.

Then Father Marquette raised his hand and made a large sign of the cross. All knelt and prayed as he gave them his last blessing. A few seconds later, both leaders knelt on the rush mats in the canoes and picked up the paddles. Father Marquette's high cheekbones were flushed with color, and his dark eyes sparkled. He smiled as he looked at Joliet. "Let's go!" cried Joliet and thrust his paddle into the water. As they rounded the long finger of land clutching at the water's edge, each leader turned and waved a last good-bye. Faintly they heard the farewell shouts of those they had left behind.

Along the indented west coast of Lake Michigan, the two canoes moved steadily. About every two hours, the men halted their pace so that the voyageurs could have a smoke, but they did not stop fully until late that afternoon when the sun was quite low.

"Are you tired, Father?" asked Joliet, after they had anchored the canoes that evening and were making camp for the night on a stretch of sandy beach.

"The joy I have felt all day gave me so much

courage that I scarcely noticed the labor of paddling," said the priest. "But I shall sleep well tonight. I will not need any bear grease to ease my muscles."

The voyageurs had already built a fire and were broiling fish on hot stones. Then Pierre Moreau, who was the best cook, put a huge kettle of corn soup on the smouldering logs.

"Put plenty of good fat pork in it, Pierre," called Joliet.

Pierre grinned and added an extra chunk of the dried meat.

At dawn, the men were up. Soon they were washed and dressed and eating big bowls of the corn soup, so thick by morning that the ladle stood upright in the kettle.

It was this way for several days. The weather was beautiful and the lake calm. When the wind was right, the men put up sails of canvas and rested from paddling. Occasionally, they saw a group of Indians on the bank, who pointed and stared but showed no hostility. In a week, the explorers were in the entrance of Green Bay. When they were about half way into the bay, the explorers came to a river.

"The Folle Avoine tribe live here," said Joliet,

pointing to the mouth of the river, which was already choked with wild oat plants, golden green in the sunshine and about a foot high. "Folle Avoine" meant wild oat.

"We will be welcome, I believe," said Father Marquette. "Our fathers have preached the gospel here for several years. Father Dablon said that these savages rarely wander from this place for there is plenty of food. The grain from the wild oats has much more meal than wild rice, and great numbers of ducks and geese come here to feed."

When the canoes drew near the village, a dozen Indians were on the bank, and some waded out to help the voyageurs. In a short time, Father Marquette and Joliet were being welcomed by the chief, and the squaws were already busy preparing a feast for them.

"Does the Black Robe mean to stay with us?" was the first question the Indians asked Father Marquette.

He shook his head with a little smile of regret. "My white brother and the five men with us go in search of the great river."

Surprise and fear showed on the faces of the tribesmen. "But the great river is very dangerous," said the chief. "It is full of monsters who will devour your canoes."

"There is a terrible demon that is heard only from a distance, but he will swallow you if you chance to pass him," said an old man, the father of the chief. "We beg the Black Robe and his white brothers to stay with us, or go back to the land from which they came."

"I thank you for your good advice," said Father Marquette. "But I have been sent to save souls, and I would gladly give my life for that."

"We will be on our guard against the evils you have mentioned," added Joliet. "But we must leave you in the morning."

The next day, after the little party left the village of the Folle Avoine tribe, the bay gradually narrowed and the water grew rough. Cautiously, they made their way, paddling quickly whenever there was a quiet stretch. Two days later, at the south end of Green Bay, they moved into the Fox River. It was so choked with growing wild oats that they could hardly paddle their canoes. Swarms of ducks and geese flew overhead and filled the air with their raucous cries as they swooped down into the grain fields.

"We should soon be at the village of De Pere at the mission of Saint Francis Xavier," said Father Marquette, checking the map. "Father Andre, who is in charge of the mission, is absent now, but I am sure the Indians who are there will welcome us."

Father Marquette's guess was correct. The little party stopped for two days at De Pere, and gained more information about the journey ahead. The rest they had was fortunate, for the remainder of the journey on the Fox River was very difficult to travel. The river was deep and winding and filled with rapids. Often the men had to carry the canoes and cargo around portages, and the sharp rocks cut their feet and tore the birch-bark covering of their craft. Each evening, the voyageurs had to mend the gashes in the sides of the canoes with long threads of spruce rootlets and fill the open seams with hot sap from the pine trees.

At last, the party moved into the broad waters of Lake Winnebago and continued slowly along the west shore until they came to the upper waters of the Fox River.

"We will soon be at the village of the Mascoutens," said Father Marquette, as he checked the notes he had made on their route. "Father Dablon said it was about a day's journey from here on the Fox River."

"I have heard that the Mascoutens are called the Fire Nations," said Joliet. "They use fire to get the copper ore from the rocks and make it into tools and utensils."

About mid-afternoon on June 7, the explorers beached their canoes at the place indicated on their rough map. There was a well-worn path leading from the water's edge. When the little party had walked about two miles, they came to a clearing in the woods. Before them on a slight hill was a great cluster of Indian huts built of rushes, and beyond, as far as they could see, were waving green fields of corn.

"Father Dablon said about three thousand savages live here," said Father Marquette. "It is the largest Indian village in the country." Then his face grew bright. "Look!" he cried.

He pointed to a large cross in the middle of the village. It was hung with white skins, red belts, and bows and arrows. "Those are gifts to their manitou," he explained. "God must have given them an abundance of food this year."

By this time, the white men had been observed, and already some of the young men were hurrying toward them with hands raised in welcome.

"We must do all we can to get information here," said Joliet. "From this point on, we will be in strange country."

The little party stayed three days with the Mascoutens. There was much feasting and speechmaking and an exchange of gifts. In the meantime, both Father Marquette and Joliet talked as much as they could to Indians who had traveled toward the Mississippi. They learned that the Wisconsin, which flowed southward, emptied into the Mississippi, and that there was a portage from the Fox River to the Wisconsin.

"But the Indians tell me that the portage is so broken by many small lakes and swamps and choked with wild oats that we may lose our way," said Father Marquette. "We no longer have the journal and map of Father Dablon to guide us."

"We will need two guides to show us the way," said Joliet to the chief as they feasted on the third day. From his pack he took out a thick wad of French tobacco. He handed it to the chief, whose eyes were glistening, for French tobacco was greatly prized by the savages. "I give you this gift," continued Joliet, "so that you will grant us this request."

"Gladly will I give you two of our young men to go part of the journey with you," said the chief, holding tight to the tobacco. "And here is a thick mat of reeds which will serve you as a bed for your voyage."

"We must rest well on this bed tonight," said Joliet later to Father Marquette. "Tomorrow, we go to a strange world."

"Our Lady will guide us," said Father Marquette confidently. His eyes were shining. Adventure was before him and a harvest of souls to be gathered.

CHAPTER

6

O_N JUNE 10, the seven Frenchmen left the village of the Mascoutens. A great crowd of Indians watched them leave. They were silent and wide-eyed with amazement, for they had heard only terrifying legends of this river on which the white men planned to travel.

For the most part, the little party carried their canoes and equipment on the portage between the Fox and Wisconsin rivers, and struggled through swamps and small lakes choked with thickets of wild oats. Finally, they reached the broad waters of the Wisconsin and got into their canoes. For a few minutes the Indian guides watched them, then strode off into the dense woods.

"We are alone now in an unknown country," said Joliet as he picked up his paddle.

The priest took out his journal and quill pen. "We must keep even more careful records now." He stopped to calculate a little. "We traveled ninety miles on the Fox River, and twenty-seven hundred paces across the portage to the Wisconsin," he noted.

"The Fox River flows northeastward from here, and the Wisconsin flows to the southwest," said Joliet, leaning over from his canoe to watch Father Marquette make a rough map of their route.

"Before we begin to float on these waters that may take us to strange lands," said the priest gravely, when he had finished his notes, "let us pray so that God will protect our persons and bring success to our voyage."

All of the men bowed their heads and folded their hands as Father Marquette led them in prayer.

The paddles dipped into the water with a uniform stroke, and the journey began. The river was wide and swift in parts. Woods and prairies and hills were on the banks. Here and there in the river were islands, some bare, others covered with trees and bushes.

On June 17, seven days after they had left the Mascoutens, and one hundred and seventy-five miles from the portage, the river grew wider and the water roughened. Swiftly, the canoes glided into another broader and fast-moving river, nearly a mile wide and flowing southward.

"It is the great river!" cried the voyageurs in awe, their paddles moving skillfully as the current changed.

"The Mississippi!" Joliet almost whispered. "At last we have reached it!" He could scarcely believe it was true. They had found the river so easily, in spite of the fact that they had no knowledge of it, except hearsay, beyond the entrance to the Wisconsin.

Father Marquette's face was shining with rapture. He had been silent as the others had spoken. "My heart is so filled with joy, I cannot say what I feel," he said in a low voice. Then he closed his eyes, and his lips moved in prayer.

Cautiously, the canoes moved into the long, sweeping curves of the river, for the current soon became slow and gentle. Rounded bluffs, three and four hundred feet high, were on both sides. Sand bars and wooded islands divided the stream.

Once the water swirled in rapid circles. "Look out!" called one of the men, and the canoes jerked quickly to one side. A great tree trunk bobbed slowly to the surface, with bare and wicked-looking branches on its sides.

"We would have been pinned like a beetle on one of those spikes, if we had been caught," said Joliet. "We must watch the water for this danger signal from now on."

Occasionally, an enormous fish bumped against a canoe with such force as to throw it out of balance. In the afternoon, the men threw out their nets and caught several sturgeon. They were very large and looked like trout except for their wide and ugly mouths.

"We'll have them for supper," said Joliet. "But tonight, I think we should make only a small fire and then return to our canoes to sleep."

"And one of us should be a sentinel at all times," added Father Marquette. So far, they had seen nothing but birds, fish, and small game, but they remembered the warnings of the friendly Mascoutens.

Again, on the second day, they saw no human beings, and Joliet decided they could land and kill some game. For the first time, they shot wild turkeys and had a fine feast in the evening. But once more, they spent the night in the canoes.

By the third day, the hills began to grow smaller

and now and then there was a stretch of prairie land. Deer and other animals were seen, and once a herd of huge, dark animals thundered across the prairie. Father Marquette stared. Some of the animals had strayed from the herd and were drinking at the water's edge. Never had he seen animals like these before. They were like cattle, only heavier, and had large heads, a foot and a half wide between the horns. On their backs was a high hump, and a thick mane, almost a foot long, hung from their heads and shoulders. The rest of their bodies was covered with short, curly hair.

"These must be the wild cattle," he said to Joliet. He recalled that he had heard that the Illinois Indians hunted for "wild cattle," and that Father Dablon had mentioned that they were also hunted by the Mascoutens.

"I have heard that they are good eating," said Joliet. "We'll try to kill one tomorrow."

The next day, Pierre Moreau killed one of the cattle. It took the strength of three men to drag the dead animal to the river's edge, so that it could be cut into pieces and roasted or dried.

At the end of a week, Joliet checked his reckonings with Father Marquette. "We have gone as far as the forty-first degree of latitude and have traveled one hundred and seventy-five miles," he said, "and so far, we have not seen a single person, nor met with any of the dangers of which the Indians warned us."

"I am happy that we have not encountered the dangers," said Father Marquette, "but," and he smiled a little wistfully, "I have traveled this long way to bring souls to God. Is it possible that there are no savages in this part of the land?"

"I cannot believe that," said Joliet. "This waterway is too fine. We must watch more closely for signs of men."

The next morning, the canoes moved nearer to the bank and the men paddled slowly. "Look!" cried Father Marquette about mid-morning. "Aren't those tracks of men?"

"Yes. And there's a path leading to the woods," cried Joliet, excitedly.

The men let their paddles rest. All stared at the footprints.

"Let us follow the path," said Father Marquette, tucking up his cassock and reaching for his broad hat.

"It may lead to the village of a warlike tribe," said Joliet, frowning a little.

"Then I may bring them to the ways of God and peace," answered the priest joyfully, but he waited for Joliet to move. He was the leader of the expedition. "What do you think we should do, Louis?"

"We should follow the path," Joliet decided. "But only you and I should go." He turned to the voyageurs. "Wait here and watch carefully. Do not let yourselves be surprised."

From a bag, Joliet selected some gifts. Then he followed Father Marquette up the slope of the bank.

The path into the woods was narrow but well-worn. Cautiously the two men followed it, pausing to listen at every crackling twig or strange animal cry, but with no word to each other. After about six miles, the path widened and grew level. Faintly, they heard the sound of barking dogs and voices of people. Step by step, they moved until they came to the edge of the trees. Joliet pointed. An Indian village was on the bank of a small stream, and on a hill were two other clusters of rush-covered huts.

"What should we do?" asked Joliet in a low voice.

"Let us ask God to aid and protect us," whispered Father Marquette. Both men bowed their heads in prayer.

The voices of the Indians were louder now, but as yet the two white men had not been noticed.

"Let us cry out as loud as we can," suggested

Father Marquette. "Perhaps, if they see my black robe, they will think we come in peace, especially since we are warning them of our coming."

"Halloo! Halloo!" both men shouted.

For a moment, all sound in the village ended except the barking of the dogs. Then a swarm of Indians rushed out from the huts and more came running from the fields. There were cries back and forth, as everyone stared and pointed, but no one reached for a bow or spear.

"They are a friendly tribe," said Joliet. His tense shoulders eased a little, and he smiled.

"They are the Illinois, I am sure," said Father Marquette excitedly. "My captive Indian at La Pointe told me about them."

Coming slowly toward them now were four old men holding long red clay pipes gayly trimmed with feathers. Occasionally, the men stopped and raised their pipes toward the sun, as if offering it a smoke.

"Those are the calumets they carry," said Father Marquette. "These tribesmen worship the sun."

He stepped forward and shouted a greeting in the Illinois dialect. The old men stopped for an instant, then hurried their pace, this time extending the calumets toward the strangers.

"It is a sign of peace," said Father Marquette.

He was confident now that they would be well received. He remembered how his captive Indian had said that his tribe thought the Black Robes would bring peace and all would be able to remain in the village.

By now the old men were only a hundred feet away, but other Indians were approaching, step by step.

"Who are you?" asked Father Marquette in the Illinois language.

Pleased surprise showed on the faces of all who heard. "We are Illinois," said one old man and held out his pipe.

Father Marquette took the pipe and pretended to smoke. He knew that otherwise he would be considered an enemy or, at least, not civil. Joliet took a good puff, sending the smoke curling upward.

In a few minutes, the two white men were being escorted to the village. In the entrance of the largest hut stood a tall, erect man, his hands extended and lifted toward the sun.

"How beautiful the sun is, oh Frenchmen, when you come to visit us!" he cried. "All our village awaits you, and you shall enter our cabins in peace."

He gestured to the white men to come into his cabin, and many of the Indians crowded in after them. Quietly, they grouped themselves in a circle around the chief and his guests as once more they were offered the calumet to smoke. In the meantime, Joliet had sent a message to the voyageurs that he and Father Marquette had been well received, but that they should remain with the canoes.

"We will go now to our great chief," said the Indian who had received them. "He wishes to hold council with you."

Led by the Indian, Father Marquette and Joliet walked with slow dignity toward a cluster of huts on the hill. Nearly everyone in the village went with them. Some ran ahead and then came back. Others climbed trees or lay in the grass to get a better view of the strangers for, so far, they had never seen Frenchmen. "How good it is, my brothers, that you should visit us," they would murmur as the white men neared them.

In the entrance of the largest cabin in the hillside village, stood the chief and two old men. All three had arms upraised and were extending their calumets to the sun. Again, the white men were welcomed and invited to smoke the calumet in the cabin.

Outside, the squaws were hurrying about as they prepared a great feast. Father Marquette knew that now was the time for speechmaking and the presentation of gifts. He rose and picked up a wad of French tobacco. The eyes of the chief brightened, and the rest of the tribe settled back in pleased expectation. There was nothing Indians enjoyed more than a long oration accompanied by gifts.

"We are journeying peacefully as far as the Sea to visit the nations dwelling on the great river," Father Marquette began, and handed the tobacco to the chief. He grasped it greedily, though he and the rest of the Indians looked dismayed at what had been said.

"No. No," they cried. "That is very dangerous."

"God, who has created you, wishes you to know Him and I have been sent for that purpose," continued the priest. He used the Indian word, "Oki," which meant "Great Spirit," since there was no word for God in their language.

This time, Father Marquette gave a knife to the chief, who quickly tested the edge and nodded approval.

"Ohey! Ohey! We wish to know Oki," cried many of the Indians, shaking their heads vigorously.

"I wish also to tell you," said Father Marquette, when they grew quiet, "that your enemies, the Iroquois, have been subdued by Governor Frontenac, the great chief of the French in Quebec."

"Ohey! Ohey!" cried the Indians again and again, and jabbered happily back and forth. The third gift from Father Marquette was a large double mirror.

"I beg you now to give us what information you have about the Sea and the nations through whom we must pass to reach it," finished Father Marquette. With this, he handed the chief several strings of beads, then sat down on the ground next to Joliet.

The chief rose slowly, first, however, pushing his gifts together. "I thank you, Black Robe, and you, Frenchman, for taking so much trouble to visit us," he said. "Never has the earth been so beautiful or the sun so bright as today." From the front ranks of the audience he motioned to a boy about ten years old. "Here is my son whom I give to you to show you my heart. He is called White Owl because he is wise, though so young, and is pure in spirit. I ask you to beg Oki to give me life and health, and to come and dwell with us." The boy was a slave, but had been adopted by the chief as his son.

Then the chief picked up his calumet and handed it to Father Marquette. "I plead with you to go no farther on your journey," he said, "but if you do, use this symbol of peace."

"I do not fear death," Father Marquette answered the chief gravely. "There would be no greater happiness for me than losing my life for Him who has made us all." Then he accepted the calumet with as much appreciation as he could show. He knew that it was even more valuable to the chief than the Indian boy who had been given to them.

Then Father Marquette sat down again next to Joliet and showed him the calumet. The bowl was made of red sandstone and was polished until it looked like marble. Bright-colored wings and heads of small birds hung from the lower side.

"There is nothing more mysterious or respected among the savages than this pipe," Father Marquette said in a low voice to Joliet. "Enemies will lay down their arms if it is shown to them, and friends will treat you with the highest honor, if a calumet is in your possession. We could have no greater gift from this chief. This is a peace calumet. If it were a war calumet, it would be decorated with red feathers."

"This may be the key that will open the way to us," whispered Joliet, who, although he did not understand the Illinois dialect, had guessed the meaning of what had been said.

In a little time, the feast was ready and all

seated themselves in a close circle around the cooking pots outside the huts. In the place of honor were the chief and his guests and the elders of the tribe. Behind them were the younger warriors, and on the fringe, the squaws and children and dogs, now minus one.

"This will be an 'eat-all' feast," whispered Joliet.

Father Marquette groaned inwardly. He had always been a moderate eater, and his years of privation during hard winter months with the savages had given him even less ability to gorge on food. But he knew that his hosts would be offended if he did not greedily devour everything that was offered.

The Indian who was in charge of the feast now approached the white men with a large wooden platter of sagamité, and fed them with a spoon as if they were children. The two white men swallowed the food obediently. Father Marquette remembered what Father Druillets had told him. "The Indians are hospitable. Never refuse their food, even though it is dirty and poorly cooked."

The second course was fish, from which the Indian carefully removed the bones and blew on the pieces to cool them before putting them in the mouths of the guests. A large cooked dog was next brought forth on a wooden platter. Perhaps, the

Indian in charge saw his guests gulp a little, because he merely showed the food to them, then passed the platter to the chief, who took a good-sized portion.

The final course was the meat of a wild cow, from which the fattest morsels were fed to the guests. By this time, even the young braves were eating more slowly, though they continued to dip their bowls into the cook pots. They wiped their grease-covered hands and faces on their hair or dirty blankets and belched loudly, but they never stopped eating.

When the last pot was scraped, the chief got up from the ground, though heavily, and beckoned to the white men to follow him. Through the streets of the village they paraded, while an orator went before them shouting to the people to come out to see these noble Frenchmen. There was no need to urge, for Indians lined the way, and as the two white men passed, threw gifts of belts, garters, and animal skins upon them.

That night, the two white men slept in the hut of the chief. About three o'clock the next afternoon, over six hundred Indians escorted them to the edge of the river where the voyageurs were waiting.

"I shall return to you in about four months," said Father Marquette to the Indians after he had blessed them. "I will reside with you then and instruct you."

"May Oki guide your way at all times," said the chief solemnly.

"Come back to us. Come back to us," came the faint cries of the savages as the canoes moved down the river.

Father Marquette looked at the calumet placed carefully on top of his box of precious instruments and roll of altar equipment. Would it be the "key" as Joliet had said?

CHAPTER

7

O N THE morning of the third day after the little party had left the Illinois Indians, they rounded a bend in the Mississippi. Suddenly, Pierre Moreau's paddle jerked to a stop. "Holy Mother of God!" he cried, and quickly made the sign of the cross.

Father Marquette, who had been reading from his breviary, looked around. The other canoe had also stopped, and Joliet as well as the voyageurs were staring in horror at the flat surface of a great wall of rock on the west bank of the river. The Indian boy, White Owl, who was in Joliet's canoe, was crouched on the floor of the canoe, his hands and arms covering his face.

The color slowly drained from Father Marquette's cheeks. He also looked in terror at the rocks. The images of two horrible animals were painted on their surface in red, black, and green. Each animal was as large as a calf, but with horns and the face and beard of a man. The body was covered with scales and had a large tail, ending like that of a fish, wound around it.

In a few seconds, the two leaders were over their fright and even smiled a little. "These must be the terrible monsters about which the savages told us," said Joliet. "After all, they are only painted creatures."

"Who could have done this work?" asked Father Marquette in wonder. "How could a painter reach those rocks?"

The composure of the leaders had restored the confidence of the voyageurs, and the canoes drew nearer to the rocks. Even White Owl straightened a little and peeked between his fingers at the figures.

"A good artist in France could not do better," said Father Marquette, studying the figures more closely. He had taken out his notebook and was making a sketch of the monsters and writing details of their appearance.

102

After one last look at the monsters, still horrible but evidently unable to do harm, the men picked up the paddles and moved south again. They were so busy discussing the paintings, that for a time they did not notice that the current of the river had become very swift. In a few minutes, their little canoes were being tossed about like chips. Great tree trunks and floating islands of bush-covered earth were rushing into the Mississippi. With all their strength, the men paddled the canoes out of the current. By this time, they knew they were at the mouth of another great river flowing from the northwest.

"What is the name of this river, White Owl?" called Father Marquette above the sound of the rushing water.

"The Indians call it 'Pekitanoui,'" answered the boy.

"That is a good name," shouted Father Marquette to Joliet. "It means 'muddy water.'"

The Missouri River was called "Pekitanoui" until 1712, and is truly a muddy stream.

The explorers stared at the Mississippi, no longer clear but a dirty brown and filled with debris.

"There are many villages of Indians along the Pekitanoui," said White Owl.

"If we return this way, I may be able to bring

the word of God to these savages," said Father Marquette hopefully.

"Perhaps the Pekitanoui leads to the Gulf of California," said Joliet, his eyes bright with speculation. If this new river did flow to the Gulf of California, the waterway to China would be discovered.

The two leaders discussed the new river they had just passed, for they were now in calmer water. It must surely lead to the California Sea, they decided. By now, they were convinced that the Mississippi emptied into the Gulf of Mexico.

Two days later, the party passed a branch of the Mississippi on the east. White Owl said that the Iroquois called it the Ohio, which meant "beautiful river." There was a village of friendly Indians here, who warned them of a "demon" in the river farther south. But the demon was only a narrow channel made by an island in the river in which the water poured with such great speed that it made a thundering noise and often caught a careless traveler in its rushing waters. The little party felt easier now. The monsters and the devouring demon of which they had so frequently been warned were past.

But there was a new enemy, small but fierce in its attacks, whose ranks were in the thousands. The days were hot and humid and mosquitoes were in thick clouds over the water. The explorers followed the pattern of the Indians. During the day, they used their canvas sails to shield them from the hot sun on the water. When they landed at night, the sails became the roof of an opensided hut under which they built a smudge fire to drive away the mosquitoes. At other times, they would make a roof of poles, sometimes covered with bark to keep off rain.

On July 10, they came to another Indian village. At first, the savages seemed hostile, but soon they permitted the party to land and generously gave them food.

"These Indians have cloth and beads and knives," said Father Marquette. "They must trade with Europeans."

He questioned the Indians in the Huron dialect which they understood in part. His face brightened as he listened to their answers.

"They said they have met men like me," he said to Joliet. "They pointed to the rosary I wear. Perhaps, these men they speak of are the Spanish friars and we are near the mouth of the river which De Soto discovered. It must be the same one on which we are now traveling."

Both Father Marquette and Joliet knew that

the mouth of a great river had been discovered and explored by the Spaniard, Hernando De Soto, in 1539. The Spanish called it the Rio del Esperito Santo, or the River of the Holy Spirit. Although it was not clearly marked on Spanish maps, the two men were certain that the river whose mouth De Soto had found was the Mississippi.

The next day as the canoes turned a bend in the river, the men saw a cluster of Indian huts near the water's edge. The men slowed their paddles a little.

"Be very careful. These are not friendly Indians," said Joliet.

There were a large number of men on the bank carrying bows, clubs, hatchets, and spears. Some climbed into canoes and moved toward the white men. Others plunged into the river and attempted to swim toward the canoes, but the current held them back.

Father Marquette rose in his canoe and held up the calumet given to him by the chief of the Illinois. The Indians on the river bank paid no attention. One tall man threw his club at the priest, and it fell with a great splash six inches from the canoe. White Owl looked at the Indians with horror. Didn't they see the symbol of peace in the hands of the Black Robe?

"Take care, Father!" cried Jacques, as another club fell near the canoe.

But the priest shook his head. "This calumet is a sign of peace," he said. "They will not fail to regard it."

Joliet looked at the young priest. He stood calm and resolute in the boat. His dark eyes were shining and his lips moved in prayer, but the arm which held out the calumet was straight and steady.

Arrows began to zing into the water near the canoe. Joliet picked up his gun. Father Marquette prayed aloud, but he kept on holding the pipe of peace aloft.

At that moment, two older men pushed forward among the Indians. They pointed to the calumet and gave sharp commands. White Owl nodded and sat back in his canoe. Slowly the younger Indians drew back. Then the two elders waded out into the water and threw their bows and arrows into Father Marquette's boat to assure him of safety. After this, they got into his canoe, and with signs indicated to the white men that they would be safe if they landed.

Under the guidance of the older men, the little party landed and soon were given food and invited to spend the night. At first, Father Marquette spoke to the Indians with signs since none of them understood any of the six dialects with which he was familiar. At last, he found one old man who knew a little of the Illinois dialect. He and ten other savages offered to go with the explorers to the village of the Arkansas which was south of them on the west bank of the river. At this village, Joliet and Marquette were told, they could get the information they sought.

The following day, the little party left with their guides. Ten leagues farther down the river, they came to the village of the Arkansas Indians who gave them a warm welcome. Here they found one young man who understood the Illinois dialect very well.

"What do you know about the Sea to the south of us?" asked Father Marquette.

"It is ten days' journey from here," was the answer. "But there is much danger if you go. There are hostile tribes to the south, and men from Europe who will bar your way."

Actually, the mouth of the Mississippi from this point was nearly one thousand miles away, and it would take much longer than ten days to reach the place where the river emptied into the Gulf of Mexico. But the explorers had other reasons for hesitating about traveling farther south. Both Father Marquette and Joliet knew that the control of the mouth of the Mississippi and the Gulf of Mexico were as important to Spain as the control of the St. Lawrence was to France. Even though Spain had made no colonies along the Gulf coast, she would not permit Frenchmen to explore the territory claimed by Spain.

The feast was ready by now and all seated themselves in the circle around the cooking pots. The serving of the food had less ceremony than with the Illinois Indians. There was an abundance of food, and the usual roasted dog, but no fruit except watermelon.

When the feast, which lasted all day, was over, the chief announced that he would dance the calumet dance as a token of the safety he promised to the white men. Everyone now moved to a large open space surrounded by shade trees under which all took their places. In the center of the open space was a reed mat on which were placed the calumet of the chief and a variety of weapons.

In the front rank of the audience was a group of men and women singers.

> "Ninahani, ninahani,
> Ninahani, nani, ongo,"

they chanted, as the chief began to move with dignified grace.

First the chief picked up his calumet and, in perfect time to the singing and the beating of drums, danced a series of figures. He offered the pipe to the sun; then spread his arms wide as if about to fly. Next he smoked the pipe himself and danced around the circle and gave it to smoke to those who sat in the front row.

"It is like a ballet," whispered Joliet.

Then the drums began to beat louder, and the chief beckoned to a warrior. He danced to the center of the ring and picked up weapons from the mat.

The chief and the warrior now pretended to fight with each other, the chief using his calumet to defend himself. Back and forth, attacking and defending, in measured steps to the music of the singing and the drums, moved the two men. At last the chief was triumphant, and the warrior fled from the ring.

As the defeated warrior left, the chief held the calumet high and began to speak.

"He is telling of his victories in war," whispered Father Marquette, guessing this from the gestures and what he had heard of the significance of the Indian dances.

Finally, the dance was over. Slowly the chief approached Father Marquette and handed him the calumet. "May there be everlasting peace between our two peoples," said the chief.

Gravely and with much ceremony, the priest accepted the gift. The calumet was similar to the one which had been given to him by the chief of the Illinois and adorned with many-colored feathers. It was a symbol of peace for the explorers.

It was dusk by now, and the chief invited the two white leaders to spend the night in his rush-covered hut. For a long time they discussed what their future plans should be.

"Should we push on or be content with the discoveries we have made so far?" asked Father Marquette.

"I believe we should turn back," said Joliet. "We know now that the Mississippi flows into the Gulf of Mexico, and if we go farther south, we would be in danger of falling into the hands of the Spaniards."

"In that case, we would lose everything we have gained so far," agreed Father Marquette.

"Let us rest here a day, then, and after that go northward," Joliet decided.

Father Marquette nodded with a tired smile. For the first time Joliet realized how weary the priest seemed. The last three days had been high with drama. At times, their lives had been at stake.

Yet with unfailing courage and confidence, the young priest had saved their expedition from disaster. Now had come a brief period of safety. But would each have courage and endurance for another test of strength? Yes, it was time for them to go back.

CHAPTER

8

THE LITTLE expedition left the village of the
Arkansas on July 17, just two months from the
time they had departed from St. Ignace. It was more
difficult now to paddle, for they were going against
the current, and the heat and mosquitoes were even
worse than on the downward voyage. But they were
aware now of the dangers they would meet, and
from the Indians they had learned of a shorter
route homeward.

"There is a river called the Illinois, which will
take us most of the way to the Lake of the Illinois,"
said Father Marquette.

"Then we should go that way, by all means," said Joliet. He gave the priest a worried look. During most of their upward journey, he had been weak and listless, and the voyageurs and Joliet had insisted that they do all the paddling.

A few days later, the canoes swept into the broad waters of the Illinois River. By this time, the weather was cooler and the mosquitoes had ceased their attacks.

"I have seen nothing like this river in all our journey," said Father Marquette the first evening they camped on the river bank. "It is so wide and deep and still." Some of his strength had returned, and he was determined now to do his share of the paddling.

"The soil is very rich," said Joliet, picking up a handful of earth. "This should be a wonderful place to make a settlement."

There were wild birds and beasts for food. Beavers were building dams along the river, and the Frenchmen had not seen beaver since they had entered the Mississippi. Vast prairies and gentle hills which made for good farmland stretched as far as they could see on both sides of the river. "I have never seen any country I like as well as this," Joliet told Father Marquette.

On the second day of their travels on the river,

a friendly Indian told the explorers of a large village called Kaskaskia farther north on the river.

"There are Illinois Indians living there," said White Owl.

The boy had been a great help on the voyage, doing his share of the paddling, and helping to fish and kill game. He traveled in Joliet's canoe most of the time, and the trader had begun to teach him French words and phrases, for he was quick to learn. Father Marquette was instructing White Owl in his prayers and catechism.

"If they are like the Illinois of your village," said Father Marquette, "they will be eager to have me tell them of the one true God." His cheeks were flushed with happiness at the thought of preaching the gospel to the natives.

Another day's journey brought the little party to Kaskaskia. This is not the town of Kaskaskia, Illinois, today, but a place about seven miles south of Ottawa, Illinois. For three days they remained in Kaskaskia, while Father Marquette with all his old fervor happily preached to the tribe.

"The chief has promised to send some young men with us to the Lake of the Illinois," said Joliet on their last evening. "From then on, we know our way."

"And I have promised the tribe that next year

I shall return to them to preach," said Father Marquette. "I shall start a mission here." Then his face saddened a little. "We are near the end of our journey, and, so far, no one has asked for baptism. If I could have saved one soul, I could consider that all of my troubles were well rewarded."

"But you have at least planted the seed, and the Illinois have begged you to return. You will reap your harvest next year," said Joliet, trying to cheer the priest.

But Father Marquette shook his head and began to read from his breviary.

The next day was Sunday. After an early Mass, the little party prepared to leave Kaskaskia. A crowd of Indians were at the river's edge, and four young men in two canoes were ready to go with the white men as far as the Lake of the Illinois.

Father Marquette raised his hand to make the sign of the cross and half chanted his blessing, knowing how much the Indians liked to have him sing the words. Just as he was ready to step into his canoe, an Indian woman, carrying a small child, pushed her way through the crowd. The child was breathing heavily and unevenly.

"See, Black Robe, my child is ready to die," cried the woman, as the tears rushed down her cheeks. "Send him to your Manitou."

A warm light came to Father Marquette's eyes. Quickly he performed the rites of baptism. He was happy now. There was one soul, at least, that he had saved.

With the Indians as guides, the little party journeyed from the Illinois to the Desplaines River. Then they carried their canoes and baggage across a muddy flat of land and pushed them into a small, sluggish stream.

"It would be a simple matter to dig a little canal from the Desplaines River to this small stream," said Joliet. "Then boats covld go all the way from the Lake of the Illinois to the Mississippi without even a portage."

About a century and a half later, the Illinois-Michigan Canal was built; it followed the route that Joliet had suggested.

Father Marquette plucked a handful of small green plants that choked the river on which they were slowly moving. "What is this river called?" he asked the Indians.

"We call it the 'Chicagou' because of the wild onion plants you are holding," said one.

The Chicago River flowed north, then east, then south for a short distance before it emptied into the Lake of the Illinois. "We are on the last stretch of our journey," said Joliet, taking a deep stroke with his paddle as they moved out into the lake.

At the end of September, the party reached Green Bay, where the expedition ended. The mission at St. Ignace was to remain in charge of Father Piercon, and Father Marquette had been instructed to take charge of the Saint Francis Xavier mission at De Pere.

Word that the little party was returning had reached De Pere. White donnés and servants, the priest who was in charge, and a crowd of Indians were waiting on the river bank at De Pere when the two canoes pulled up to the shore.

"It is too late now for me to journey to Quebec," said Joliet. "The ice will form before I reach the Saint Lawrence."

"Then stay here at least for a time," urged Father Marquette. "We will need the winter months to rewrite our accounts and correct our maps."

The winter months were busy ones for the two men. In addition to working on the record of their trip, Father Marquette was busy with the work of his new mission, and Joliet explored the surrounding country.

Like all the Jesuit priests who wrote the accounts to be published in the annual *Jesuit Rela-*

tions, Father Marquette added much scientific information to his record of the trip. He listed and described the various animals, trees, fruits, and berries of each region the explorers had traveled. In detail, he wrote about the appearance, character, and manner of living of the various tribes they had encountered. The manner of harvesting the wild oats, and the special fishing methods of the Folle Avoine or Wild Oat tribe were fully stated.

There were also discoveries that the explorers had made in addition to finding the Mississippi. They had found a plant which, the Indians said, would cure snakebite when chewed. North of the Ohio River, they had located rich deposits of iron ore.

Throughout the journey, both men had used their instruments of navigation, and they had measured and recorded the latitude of their various stopping places, and the depth of the waterways they had traveled. All in all, Father Marquette's account was a very comprehensive affair.

In the early spring, Joliet left for the Sault, for this was where the warehouse of his family was located. Before leaving De Pere, Joliet gave a copy of his account of the voyage to Father Marquette.

"We both have had the same experiences and have seen the same people and places," said Joliet,

119

"but, perhaps our viewpoint was different. I shall take my account to Governor Frontenac, but will leave this one with you for safekeeping."

"God will be with you on your journey home," said Father Marquette. "I shall pray each day for your safety."

Joliet decided to take the two voyageurs who had come with him from Montreal as well as White Owl, the Indian boy. He was quite attached to the boy, and planned to send him to school in Quebec.

"White Owl is so diligent and obedient," said Joliet. "Already he knows how to speak French, and is learning to read and write."

"I have instructed him in the faith," said the priest, who was also fond of the boy. "He should be ready for baptism by the time you reach Quebec."

"I will see that he remembers his prayers and his catechism," promised Joliet.

CHAPTER

9

At the Sault, Joliet gathered furs to take back to Quebec and made another copy of his journal. This he left in the care of the Jesuit priest who was in charge of the mission at the Sault.

In May, Joliet, with his two voyageurs and White Owl, started for Quebec. They went by way of the Ottawa River, high now from the spring thaws and filled with foaming, white-crested rapids. It was a difficult route, but the shortest way home, and Joliet was eager to tell his story of the voyage to Governor Frontenac.

It was good once again as they traveled along

the Ottawa River to see the low-built, white-washed houses of the farmers built close to the water's edge. Each had its long, narrow strip of farmland in the back, for not only did the farm people want companionship, but easy transportation on the river.

"One can see all of New France by traveling along the St. Lawrence and its branches," said Joliet to his companions.

The voyageurs shouted happily to the people. Most of them seemed to be outdoors. Men in wide pantaloons and wooden clogs worked in the fields or kitchen gardens; women in full-skirted calico dresses, barefooted or with wooden clogs, washed clothes in the river or baked bread in the big outdoor ovens; children fished or played along the bank. All waved and called to those in the canoe.

White Owl twisted and turned in the canoe to see this new kind of life. Each evening, the travelers stopped at a farmhouse and told their story to a wide-eyed audience, meanwhile eating heartily of abundant, home-cooked meals.

By July 1, they were at the La Chine rapids below Montreal. "Should we put our goods in carts and walk around the rapids?" asked one of the voyageurs. This was the usual procedure for traders, for the La Chine rapids were the most dangerous ones on the St. Lawrence River.

Joliet frowned. It was an eight-mile walk to Montreal and it was already late in the afternoon. He doubted if they would reach the town before nightfall.

"This is a good day," he said. "We've gone through twenty rapids in these canoes. Surely, we can manage this one."

The rowers paddled skillfully along the waterway. They talked joyfully of soon seeing Montreal where the voyageurs lived. Suddenly, both canoes were drawn into a swift current. In a few minutes, in spite of desperate paddling, the boats were overturned. With horror, Joliet saw the strong box in which were his records and instruments go tumbling into the water. The churning waters swept over the men. With all his strength, Joliet tried to swim to the bank. Once, he tried desperately to reach White Owl, only to see the Indian boy drawn swiftly away, and then lost in the boiling waters. He caught a glimpse of the voyageurs, also struggling and tossed about, until they, too, were gone from sight.

Somehow, Joliet reached the bank and threw himself on a flat rock. For a long time, he lay exhausted until he heard voices from the top of the precipice far above where he lay. He managed to raise himself a little and shouted for help. Down the river bank, two fishermen came to his aid, though the rocks were so steep and slippery that a half dozen times they almost lost their footing. Between them, they carried Joliet by an easier route to Montreal. Here in the home of his friend, Jacques Le Ber, a wealthy merchant, he rested and recovered his strength.

The whole town rejoiced at the story of the expedition, though the people were saddened at the loss of the voyageurs and the Indian boy. But Joliet brooded bitterly. White Owl, whom he had grown to love as a son, had been drowned. The two brave voyageurs who had shared all his hardships ever since they had left Montreal had also lost their lives. All of the furs he had collected and the records he had made so carefully were at the bottom of the river. "And all because I was in too great a hurry to get to Montreal," he told Jacques Le Ber remorsefully.

In just a few days, however, Joliet's buoyant spirits returned. He was eager now to get to Quebec. In the middle of the week, he left Montreal and reached Quebec on Sunday. At once, he went to the home of his mother, where his brother Zachary and his family were having Sunday dinner. Although they had heard through Indian traders that Joliet and Father Marquette had returned from their journey, the whole family had a day of happy feasting as they listened to the account of the expedition. There were many candles lit at the family altar and prayers of gratitude when he told of his rescue by the two fishermen.

"If only my little Indian boy, White Owl, could have been saved," said Joliet sadly. "I learned to love him as a son, and planned to enroll him at Bishop Laval's Little Seminary for the young boys."

"Never mind, Louis," comforted his mother. "Now that you have found the great river, you can have a wife and sons of your own." Already, she was listing the pretty girls of good families in Quebec who would make a fine wife for her son.

The next day, Joliet wrote a letter to Governor Frontenac since he was not on close terms with him, and told of the accident that had occurred at the La Chine rapids. "Except for this shipwreck," Joliet ended his letter, "your Excellency would have had a quite interesting relation. But all that I saved is my life."

On the receipt of the letter, the Governor requested Joliet to come in person to make his report. The old Chateau St. Louis was furnished as richly as Governor Frontenac could command, and he himself was dressed as elegantly as if he were at Versailles. He was a tall, lean man, with a big nose and wide mouth. Although he was only in his mid-fifties, his face was deeply lined, for he had led a vigorous life of campaigning before he had come to New France. He was cordial in his welcome of Joliet and was eager to hear all the details of the expedition.

Joliet explained in the beginning why he had come to the Governor without papers or maps. "But I am sure that I remember everything that happened, Your Excellency," said Joliet. "Father Marquette and I kept careful records, and we wrote and rewrote the account and made the maps during the winter."

As the day went on, and Joliet told about the expedition and made a rough map of the route, the Governor nodded approval. "But I shall want you to write all of this down and make the map while it is still fresh in your mind," he said after Joliet had told his story. "I shall send it immediately to Colbert, our minister in France."

Joliet also made several visits to Father Dablon. The priest had bitter news for him on his first visit. Father Dablon had just learned that the mission at the Sault had been burned to the ground, and that everything, including the copy of Joliet's journal, had been lost.

"But there is still the copy I left with Father Marquette," said Joliet hopefully. "I am sure you will receive his own account as well as the one I wrote very soon."

Once more, Joliet repeated in detail the story of the voyage down the Mississippi, while Father Dablon made careful notes. As soon as he received the account from Father Marquette, the superior planned to compile all that he had learned and write it for the *Jesuit Relations.*

Joliet told Father Dablon of his dream of colonizing along the Illinois River, and of the water route he had planned from Quebec to the Mississippi. "All that is necessary is to dig a canal about half a league long on the land we portaged between the Desplaines and Chicago rivers," said Joliet.

Joliet also told Father Dablon how ill Father Marquette had been on the return journey. "But he is anxious to go back to the Illinois Indians at Kaskaskia," said Joliet. "He is praying that God will give him the strength to make the journey."

"We shall all pray here for his recovery," said Father Dablon. "As soon as he is well enough, I shall give him permission to go to Kaskaskia."

Quickly, Joliet began to write his story of the expedition for Governor Frontenac. When it was finished, he had the best scribe in Quebec make a copy and write a complimentary inscription for the Governor. Joliet also changed the name of the

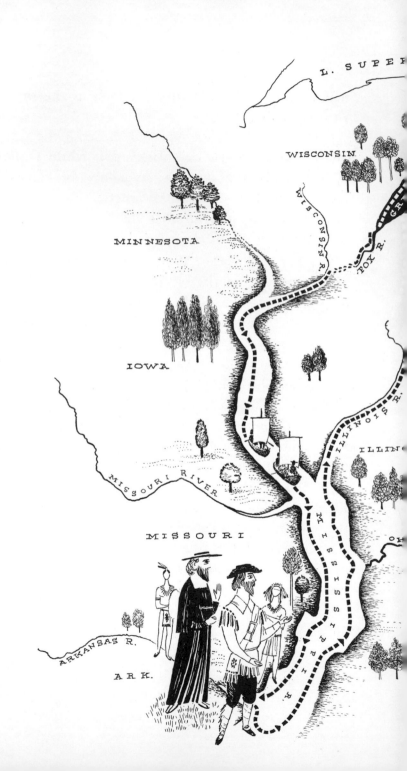

L. SUPER

WISCONSIN

WISCONSIN R.

FOX R.

GR

MINNESOTA

IOWA

MISSOURI RIVER

MISSOURI

ILLINOIS R.

ILLIN

MISSISSIPPI

OH

O

ARKANSAS R.

ARK.

SAULT STE. MARIE

ST. IGNACE

L. HURON

L. ONTARIO

L. MICHIGAN

MICHIGAN

L. ERIE

The
Route of
Father
Jacques Marquette
and Louis Joliet

*May—September
1673*

Mississippi River to Bruade River in honor of the family name of Governor Frontenac.

When everything was completed, Joliet went in person to the Chateau St. Louis to present the documents to the Governor. Frontenac was delighted to receive the manuscript and map, and flattered to have the river named in his honor. "I shall send this immediately to Colbert," he said.

"Nothing remains to me but my life and the ardent desire to employ it in any service your Excellency may direct," said Joliet, before leaving the Governor.

Perhaps because he was more interested in the explorations now being made by La Salle, Governor Frontenac did not call on Joliet to make further explorations. In October, 1675, Joliet, now a fur trader, married Claire-Francois Bissot, the great granddaughter of Louis Hebert, the first Frenchman to settle in Quebec as a farmer. The young couple had their home in the Lower Town of Quebec near the warehouse of the Joliet family.

In 1679, Joliet was sent on a voyage to Hudson Bay, and for this and other voyages, he was given several land grants, the most important being Anticosti Island in the St. Lawrence River. Joliet was a wealthy man until 1690, when the English invaded Canada and he lost all of his property. He was never able after that to recover his former wealth and property and was in actual poverty when he died in 1690. It was a long time before his name received the credit it deserved.

CHAPTER

10

ALL DURING the summer of 1674, Father Marquette took good care of his health, so that by September his strength had returned. In the meantime, he had sent an Indian runner with his account of the trip and a map he had made to Father Dablon in Quebec. The map showed that the explorers had traveled 2900 miles in all; they had gone 1700 miles down the river and 1250 on the return trip. This map can be seen today in the archives of St. Mary's College in Montreal. It is the only autographed document by a member of the expedition.

Late in October, Father Marquette received

permission from Father Dablon to go to Kaskaskia.

"We will leave as soon as we can prepare our canoe and provisions," Father Marquette said joyously to his voyageurs. Both Jacques Largillier and Pierre Porteret had remained in De Pere during the winter. They were devoted to Father Marquette and planned to go with him if he went on another voyage.

"But we may not be able to reach Kaskaskia before the ice forms," said Jacques.

"God will help us, I am sure," said the priest confidently.

About noon on October 25, 1674, the little party started traveling along the eastern shore of Green Bay. As on his first expedition, Father Marquette took writing material and kept a brief diary of each day's events. This weather-stained document can also be seen at St. Mary's College. Two days after they started, at Sturgeon Bay, they met a party of nine canoes of Illinois and Pottawatomie Indians who were also on their way to Kaskaskia. They invited Father Marquette to join them.

"Do not leave us at any time, Black Robe," the leader warned him. "We know the lake better than you do, and you may need us."

"God has come to our aid as I promised you," the priest happily told his voyageurs.

Slowly, the little fleet of canoes traveled south-ward along the western shore of Lake Michigan. Rain fell in torrents, and the canoes were tossed on the giant waves. Sometimes, the little party was forced to camp on the beach for two or three days.

Each morning, when it stormed, the voyageurs took bits of the tobacco from their wad and threw them into the storm-torn lake. "Blow, blow, old woman!" cried Pierre, as the shreds of tobacco flew away in the wind.

"That old woman lake is mad today," said Jacques. "We give her something to smoke, and she will get quiet."

But Father Marquette set up his rude altar in a sheltered spot and said Mass. He knew that al-though his voyageurs were deeply religious their age-old superstitions were too strong for him to at-tempt to change them.

By the end of November, the weather grew colder. Snow fell in thick flakes, and ice began to form along the edge of the lake. On December 4, when the party reached the entrance to the Chicago River, a foot of snow covered the ground. Blocks of ice floated in the river, but the canoes moved slowly until they were in the south branch. At last, they were forced to stop, for the river was frozen solid and the ice about a foot thick.

"We must build a cabin here and wait until the snow melts, Father," said Pierre. He looked anxiously at the priest, whose illness had returned with the cold weather.

"We still have plenty of corn, and the hunting should be good," said Jacques, trying to be cheerful.

"It is God's will," said Father Marquette. It was hard not to be able to go to Kaskaskia, but he knew it would be certain death if they continued the journey.

In two days, the men had completed a cabin of rough logs, with a slanting roof so that the snow would not accumulate. The site was at the intersection of Damen and Twenty-fourth streets in Chicago, Illinois, and is marked today by a cross. By the time the cabin was built, the Indians with whom they had traveled had left, carrying their canoes and supplies, for they could endure the hardships of winter much better than the white men. Before the Indians left, they traded three ox skins for some French tobacco.

The long winter passed. Other Indians learned that Father Marquette was in their area. They told this to La Toupine, who had been with the explorers on their first journey, and who was now living in a cabin with a doctor about fifty miles from Father Marquette's cabin. The doctor and an Indian brought the priest and his voyageurs a sack of corn and some dried blueberries, as well as some medicine for Father Marquette's ailment. After several days, the doctor left for Kaskaskia, after confessing and receiving communion from Father Marquette.

"I shall send Jacques with you to Kaskaskia," said Father Marquette to the doctor. "He can tell the Illinois that my illness has prevented me so far from seeing them, and that I may even have some difficulty in going to them in the spring, if it continues."

Two days later, Jacques returned with several of the Illinois. They brought large sacks of corn-meal and dried pumpkin and some beaver skins. "We do not want you to be hungry or cold, Black Robe," said the leader. "But we would like you to give us some powder for our guns."

"You can kill the game better with your bows and arrows," said Father Marquette. He knew that the Indians were poor marksmen with guns, and liked to fire them only because of the noise they made.

"But we could use the guns against our enemies," the leader protested.

Father Marquette shook his head. "I will not give you powder to make war," he said. "I wish to restore peace among the tribes." He took some beads and knives and mirrors from his box of gifts. "Take these to the elders of your tribe and tell them to give them to the people." He raised his hand and blessed the Indians.

"Stay with us, Black Robe, until you die," begged the leader. "Tell us of your God."

"I will come to your village in the spring," Father Marquette promised. He was feeling much better now and was confident that he would be able to go to Kaskaskia.

"Let us pray to God to restore my health," Father Marquette suggested to the voyageurs a few days after the Indians had left. "I have only a weakness now in my stomach. I am sure, if we pray, God will give me the strength to go to the mission."

Each day after that, the three men prayed with great fervor, and each day, Father Marquette's health and spirits improved.

In the last week of March, Jacques noticed cracks in the ice. He moistened his finger and held it up. "The south wind is beginning to blow!" he called excitedly. "The river is breaking."

All that night, the ice broke with loud crashing sounds. By morning, the river had risen almost to their cabin floor. "We must pack our belongings and move to higher ground," said Father Marquette.

Even though the men moved quickly, they scarcely had time to reach a low hill a short distance to the south. They put their supplies in the trees and slept on the ground wrapped in their fur robes. By next morning, there was a slight freeze and the water fell a little. "The ice has drifted away. I believe we can depart," said Father Marquette. The place where they stopped is at the intersection of Harlem Avenue and Forty-ninth Street in Chicago and is marked by a large monument.

In a short time, their canoe was packed, and the journey began down the Chicago River. When they had gone about nine miles, they came to the place where they had portaged the preceding year. But here the water was twelve feet high and once again, they waited on a high rise of ground for the water to recede.

Ducks and geese flew over their stopping place in large numbers and they still had a good supply of corn, so that they did not lack for food. A week passed, however, before they were able to move into the Desplaines River. A few miles from where they started, they met the French doctor with a canoe full of furs. As it was too cold to carry his canoe, and he could not manage it alone, he decided to bury his furs and go with them to Kaskaskia.

On April 8, the two canoes reached the village.

Here a crowd of Indians were waiting to receive them. Some waded out into the cold water to help with the unloading. Jacques carried Father Marquette pick-a-back so that he would not have to step into the chilling river. The Indians swarmed around the priest as he was escorted to the cabin of the chief. They chattered and smiled happily if they were even able to touch his robe.

"It is as if you were an angel from Heaven come to visit them," said the doctor, who had also been warmly received.

For the next two days, Father Marquette instructed the chief and the elders and went from one crowded cabin to another to preach his faith. It was Easter Week, and he wished to tell the story of the crucifixion and resurrection of Christ to all the people.

"Will you arrange for an assembly outdoors, so that I may speak to the whole village at once?" he asked the chief on the eve of Holy Thursday.

The chief happily agreed.

The next morning, all of the tribe gathered at a beautiful tree-encircled prairie near the village. Fresh mats and skins were laid in the center. Around this inner circle, Father Marquette hung four pieces of Chinese taffeta, to which were attached large, brightly colored pictures of the Blessed

139

Virgin. Nearest the priest, five hundred chiefs and elders were seated, and standing behind them were about a thousand young men. Beyond them were women and children, for this was a very large village.

For nearly two hours, Father Marquette spoke to the crowd. Then he said Mass and gave communion to the voyageurs and the French doctor, while the Indians watched with reverent awe. On Easter Sunday, Father Marquette again said Mass and gave communion to the Frenchmen, and once more the Indians came in large numbers.

"I must leave you now," Father Marquette said the next day to the chief. "My sickness forces me to return to my mission at De Pere."

"But you will come back to us," begged the chief. "My people wish to know your God."

"Either I will come back myself, or I will send another Black Robe in my place," the priest promised.

The following morning, Father Marquette and the voyageurs left Kaskaskia. A dozen Indians traveled with them for nearly one hundred miles, arguing with each other for the honor of paddling the canoe of the Black Robe or carrying his provisions.

Shortly after the Indians left them, the voyageurs paddled their way into the Lake of the Illinois. They went by a new route along the southern and eastern side of the lake, for Father Marquette realized that he did not have long to live, and he now wished to return to St. Ignace.

The priest lay exhausted on a reed mat in the canoe, too feeble even to move without help. In the evening, the men carried him to shore as if he were a child. Through the long day, his lips moved in prayer as he prepared himself for death. On Friday, May 17, after they had camped, Father Marquette called the men to the bed of boughs they had made for him. "God will take me tomorrow," he whispered. "We must be prepared."

At intervals the next day, as the canoe moved northward, the priest told the voyageurs what kind of place should be chosen for his grave and how they should bury him. Tears ran down the cheeks of the men, and the rhythm of their paddling was broken as their shoulders shook with their sobs.

In the afternoon, Father Marquette noticed a little rise of ground near a river that emptied into the lake. "Let us stop here," he murmured. "My time has come."

"But it is early, Father. Should we not go on?" asked Pierre. He was hoping the priest might live until they reached St. Ignace.

Just then, a strong wind blew white-capped

waves toward the shore. "Let us land," called Jacques. "The rough water will be hard for our Father."

Tenderly the men carried the priest ashore. They built an open-sided shelter and made a small fire, but they were so stricken with grief that they scarcely knew what they were doing. The hours passed slowly. Occasionally, Father Marquette spoke. He thanked the men for what they had done and heard their confessions. He gave them a paper on which he had written his own confession to give to Father Dablon. At last it grew dark.

"Sleep now," he said. "I will call you when my hour is near."

Two hours later, he called and the men came immediately, for they had been watching near the fire. They drew near, and he put his arms around them to comfort them as they wept. From a cord around his neck he unfastened his crucifix. "Hold it high before my eyes," he whispered to Pierre.

For a time, Father Marquette's lips moved in prayer. Then he murmured, "I thank God for letting me die as St. Francis did in a wretched cabin in the midst of the forest."

There was a long silence, though his lips were still moving. "Mother of God, remember me," he said aloud. A few minutes later, he opened his eyes

142

wide and gazed upward at the crucifix. His whole face shone as if at the sight of God. Then he closed his eyes for the last time in a gentle sleep.

When dawn came, the men arranged the body of the priest and buried it as he had instructed them. In his folded hands were his rosary and crucifix. Then while Pierre rang their little chapel bell, Jacques placed a large wooden cross near the grave. In a little while, the voyageurs were paddling their canoe northward on their way to Father Dablon in Quebec. Carefully wrapped in a large sheet of birch bark was the journal that Father Marquette had kept on his last journey, and the letter of confession he had written.

Two years later, a group of Indians who had become Christians while Father Marquette was at La Pointe were hunting on the eastern shore of Lake Michigan. In the spring, they came to his grave, still marked by the wooden cross.

"We should carry the bones of our good Father to the mission at St. Ignace," the leader decided.

The bones were placed in a birch-bark box and the Indians made the journey to St. Ignace. At the mission, the box was placed in a vault in the middle of the church. There the bones were to lie, revered by all who came to St. Ignace, until the little church was destroyed.

Two centuries later, a Jesuit priest, Father E. Jacker, searched the ruins of the church and found the bones which were identified as those of Father Jacques Marquette. Today a new church has been built, and some of the bones are buried under a monument in front of the church. The remainder of the bones are at Marquette University in Milwaukee, Wisconsin.

In many places in the United States, and especially in the area of their expedition, there are monuments and markers to the memory of Father Marquette and Louis Joliet. Their names live on in the history of the great and fertile region they explored.